Camp Reunion

Caroline B. Cooney

Teens · Mandarin

2 204502 071

First published in the USA 1988
by Bantam Books, Inc.
First published in Great Britain 1990
by Teens, an imprint of Mandarin paperbacks
Michelin House, 81 Fulham Road, London SW3 6RB

Mandarin is an imprint of the Octopus Publishing Group

Copyright © 1988 by Caroline B. Cooney

ISBN 0 7497 0271 0

A CIP catalogue record for this title
is available from the British Library

Printed in Great Britain
by Cox & Wyman Ltd, Reading

1

Violet wanted to go to the camp reunion so much that every morning she marked off a square on her calendar so she could watch the approach of the great day. And every day she changed her mind and decided not to go. It had been a great summer, much to her surprise. Her campers had adored her, and she'd found a fabulous boyfriend at camp. The idea of a reunion sounded cozy and crowded and huggy: people crying, "Vi! I'm so glad to see you!"; people giving her bear hugs, saying, "Why didn't you write? You were the only one I really wanted to hear from!"

But what if it turned out to be the kind of reunion where people were only glad to see other people, and not her? What if the hugs and kisses steered around her, and she was abandoned in the middle of a huge, barren hotel lobby, with nobody who even remembered her from last summer?

And she would have to talk to her now ex-boyfriend, Jamie, in public. Everybody would be watching. Jamie would be bored. She would be in agony.

Vi and Jamie had conducted a very public romance. What choice had there been? The privacy of camp is zero. No clump of evergreens, no shadow behind the dining hall, no woodsy trail was safe from little spies. Her camper Claudia had actually kept a tally of known kisses. "Let's see," Claudia would say, tapping a pencil against her teeth. "We've got four kisses that Marissa's cabin witnessed. Two kisses Janey watched, and—"

Every week last summer, Vi had gotten one night off. Charles, the camp manager, reluctantly changed Jamie's schedule to permit Jamie to have the same night off. (By the time Charles had agreed to this, there had been only four nights off left in the summer.) When Violet got back from her dates, no matter how late it was, no matter how exhausted her campers should have been from a day of camping, hiking, swimming, canoeing, and dancing, her entire cabin had been waiting up.

They had wanted details.

"Nothing romantic," they would tell Vi firmly. They could read about romance in books. From her they wanted anatomical material. "But what was the kiss like?" they would demand. "What exactly did he do? And for how many seconds? And what did you do? Show us what your face looked like then. Did your hair get in your eyes?"

Vi could just imagine the reunion: Claudia with her kiss book open, and a dozen little girls giggling, while Vi had to admit out loud that Jamie had never called her after the summer was over.

The fantasies her cabin had come up with! Jamie and Vi would date forever, the girls decided, and have children, and tell the children how their parents had fallen in love at Camp Girl-Meets-Boy. (Everybody shortened Camp Menunkechogue to Camp Men, but Vi had carried it a step further. "It's Camp Girl-Meets-Boy," she'd explained to her campers. "And I came to Camp Men to meet the perfect boy.")

But the moment he drove out the camp gate, Jamie forgot Vi. Vi had wept more nights than she cared to remember. What if she cried at the reunion? What if Jamie sauntered up (in the formal clothing she had hardly ever seen on him, because at camp Jamie prided himself on being clothed only from the waist down) and she burst into tears? She who had kissed and loved him—was she supposed to shake hands? Ask after his mother? Offer him a stick of gum?

Better to sit home that terrifying Saturday, alone, with a mirror and depression.

Violet's mother was exasperated with all this. "Honey, there will be hundreds of people there. And I promise you, not a single one will care whether Jamie asked you out after the summer ended."

Was this supposed to be comforting?

What good was life if people didn't care what Violet was doing?

Her mother's attempts to comfort Vi hardly ever worked. Vi's mother felt humans were paltry stars in a vast Milky Way. Vi preferred to think of herself as the sun, with everybody else revolving around her.

"Mother," said Vi, getting down to essentials, "I'll need a new dress."

"Violet, it's a camp reunion. You don't need a new dress, you need an old T-shirt."

Violet counted the calendar days left. Very few for a major shopping expedition. She flung open closet doors and bureau drawers to prove how inadequate her wardrobe was. "Mother, it is not simply a camp reunion. It's also, as you well know, Charles and Alicia's wedding."

They were in Vi's room surrounded by half-open drawers. School for Vi and work for her mother were over for the day. Vi peeled off her wool pants and extra long L. L. Bean shirt, while her mother got out of her hospital uniform. Around the house they both preferred sweat suits.

"I think that is idiotic," said Vi's mother, now down to pale green lace bra and panties. "What kind of people would have a combination camp reunion and wedding? Alicia's family clearly has no sense of etiquette."

Vi flicked her sweatpants at the wall with irritation. "Mother!" They were at a stage where it was difficult to chat for sixty seconds without confrontation. "It is *not* a combination reunion and wedding. They're not going to mix the camp pledge with the wedding vows. It's just that there's a camp reunion planned for the Saturday after Thanksgiving anyway, and since Charles and Alicia want the same people to be at their wedding, it's logical to

4

have the reunion in the afternoon and the wedding in the evening."

Now they were both in nothing but bra and panties. They glared at each other, like sumo wrestlers. "I don't think it's logical at all," said her mother. "I think it's queer."

Vi stalked into the bathroom and looked in the mirror, mentally dressing herself in a wedding gown.

Of course, Alicia was marrying Charles. That was a silly decision. Vi had no use for Charles whatsoever. The fact that it was Charles that Alicia would meet at the altar did dampen Vi's enthusiasm for the whole thing. Still—a wedding. Who could dislike weddings? And it was so romantic that the camp nurse had fallen in love with the camp owner/manager.

Vi's mother began poking through Vi's sweat-shirt collection. She'll stretch them, thought Vi, but said nothing.

"I detest weddings," said her mother, stretching the Ski Vermont sweatshirt. "You know they're going to get divorced in a year, anyhow, and you've wasted all that money on a gift."

"They are not going to get divorced!" shouted Vi. Although she personally would have a marriage to Charles annulled by midnight. Charles was very suspicious of Vi. He thought that any girl who brought hot rollers and a lighted makeup mirror to a Maine wilderness camp was bound to cause trouble. ("If you leave those appliances of yours plugged in, Violet," Charles had yelled at her once, "and your cabin catches fire, and the

5

forest catches fire, and all the innocent furry little animals . . ."

"I am not going to murder anybody, Charles!" Vi had screamed back. "I'm just going to have curly hair, all right?")

She and Charles had never reached friendship. Or even armed truce. Vi had been invited to the wedding because of Alicia. Violet decided to sit on Alicia's side of the church, or hotel as the case was here, and possibly make a face at Charles when nobody was looking.

"Why are you always talking divorce these days, Mother?" demanded Violet. "It's not very romantic. Not everybody in the whole world is getting divorced."

"Sure feels like it," her mother muttered.

This was because Vi's older sister, Jasmine, had just abandoned her husband of two years to come back home and live. There was no real reason, as Jasmine was the first to admit. Her husband was not a drunk, a druggie, or a violent man. He earned money regularly and took out the garbage and cooked on alternate nights. "I was bored," said Jasmine.

"You promised to love, honor, and cherish that man till death do you part," screamed her parents. "And we gave you the most splendid wedding we could afford—in fact, more than we could afford—and you abandon him *because you're bored*?"

Vi's older sister said that, if all her mother and father cared about was the money, and not their daughter's happiness, then she was very disappointed in their values.

"Our values!" screamed the parents.

And so on, and so forth, night after night, until in that household, the very word wedding was enough to make people draw their weapons. Violet decided not to start yet another argument about weddings. She needed the whole evening to consider what her wedding gift was going to be, anyhow.

Still, the problem of what to wear loomed large. Vi kept waiting for the appropriate minute to reinforce the idea that she needed a new dress, but there never was such a moment. Finally she went to her grandmother. This was a strategical error, because Grandma was even more upset over Jasmine than anybody, and practically had a heart attack when Vi mentioned weddings.

That's all I need, thought Vi, fixing her grandmother tea and cookies. Grandma having cardiac arrest at my feet because I ask for a dress. Then Mother and Dad will *really* know their two daughters have sick values.

In the end, Violet went to Jasmine. "Listen," she said to her sister. "You've wrecked my family life and I'm forgiving you only if you buy me a dress."

This appealed to Jasmine, not because she worried about Vi's family life, but because shopping was her favorite activity. Jasmine knew every size-eight rack from the local mall to San Francisco. Jasmine leaped into the project with enthusiasm. (Jasmine loved weddings; in fact she hoped to have a second of her own, one of these days.) So Vi ended up with a new reunion outfit (which also looked good on Jasmine) *and* a new wedding outfit (which looked excellent on Jasmine), because Jasmine understood these were not the same event and a person could not appear badly dressed at either one, not when important things like Jamie were at stake. Jasmine even loaned Vi a sexy, silken gown and peignoir that had been a shower gift to Jasmine.

Vi felt like a bride herself in the shimmering folds of ivory lace and silk. Would the other girls sharing the hotel suite ever be impressed now!

But thinking of those girls made Vi quiver. For it was not really Jamie who worried her most. It was Marissa.

Marissa and Vi had shared responsibility for the twelve-year-old girl campers. They were cool with each other at first. Marissa was the kind of camp counselor who could identify constellations and paw prints and leaves, while Vi was the kind who was good at hair conditioners. Marissa loved how the cabins were nestled in the forest, while Violet felt that every crackling twig probably meant Big Foot come to kill her. Vi brought so much clothing and makeup, she needed help towing it up the cliff path to her cabin, while Marissa brought so little you would have thought she was staying half an hour, not ten weeks.

Summer had passed.

Vi struggled with campers who wet the bed and insisted on playing the trumpet when they were not musical, and who, instead of sleeping through the night like normal people, were always having M&M's fights at two in the morning, or pretending to be rats at three in the morning.

Marissa's cabin always won inspection, and swam like dolphins, and knew the middle verses to all the camp songs. Vi's cabin was always late for supper because they were practicing using her eye shadow.

Slowly, reluctantly, Vi and Marissa had become friends. By the end of summer they were inseparable friends. They could talk about everything. Whether Sinclair ("Call me Sin") Franklin would ever love Marissa the way Marissa loved Sin. Whether Cathy deserved to be shot, or if Charles should be pushed off a cliff. The last day of camp, they had wept saying good-bye, and promised to be friends forever.

But Marissa had never telephoned Vi. Never written. And something—what?—had held Vi back, too. Perhaps they had not been friends at all, and the closeness that had developed between them over July and August was only a truce. Perhaps when Marissa returned to her own high school and her own friends, Vi had paled in comparison and Marissa forgot her.

Vi knew now about summer romances.

She had not known there could be summer friends.

Oh, what if nobody at the reunion remembered her?

What if Marissa said vaguely, "Oh, hi—uh—let's see—it's . . ."

What if Jamie was hugging somebody else when Vi got there?

What if Cathy said in her cruel way, "I think it's Violet. Were you Violet?"

I won't go, thought Vi. Better to miss the whole reunion than risk that.

"Yes, you will too go," said Jasmine. "If you think I bought you all that stuff and you're not wearing it, you're wrong. You're going."

2

Cathy Coatsworth was breathtakingly beautiful.

Her looks could quiet a room. Her boyfriend, Channing, had called her his golden dove. Channing, who'd been in college, seemed never to worry about classes or papers. He was handsome in the smooth sort of way that would have given him the role of European royal lover if they had starred together in a movie.

Cathy used to love to appear in public with Channing. When she and Channing drifted into a room, motion and conversation stopped, while everybody paused to pay homage to their beauty.

Channing had had friends everywhere. She and Channing always had somebody to meet, and her social schedule was crammed beyond belief. She loved boasting about it. She could think of no teenage girl whose life was so busy.

Last summer, when Channing had told Cathy he had to make a few trips to South America, she'd loved hearing that. He was only twenty, yet he sounded like an oil tycoon or a diplomat. But she hadn't known what to do with herself. Her parents were going to Europe, and her older brother and sister were busy, too. She hadn't wanted to be home, hanging around alone. And she hadn't wanted to go to Europe with her parents. Finally, she'd decided to be a dance counselor at an overnight camp. She'd loved the idea of being worshipped by hundreds of little girls, who would all want to grow up to be exactly like her.

When September came, Channing thought it was hysterically funny that Cathy, of all people, the golden dove, had been a camp counselor. Cathy was an excellent storyteller. She routinely had people's eyes on her, but after her summer camp experience, she told funny stories and captured their ears, too. "Well, there was Marissa, pitiful thing," Cathy would begin, gluing the audience to herself. "Or was her name Melissa? She didn't have much personality. She was always off rejoicing in the scent of hemlocks on the nature trail. Marissa's idea of a big day was making fern bookmarks in arts and crafts."

They would be in a disco or a new place to eat, and Cathy would reinvent her camp stories to get an easy laugh. "You should have heard all these kids saying their little pledge," Cathy would mock, placing her manicured nails on her heart! "They were so serious. *I promise to show the world I am a Camp Menunkechogue girl.*"

"Camp what?" Everybody would giggle.

"Camp Menunkechogue," Cathy would say, in her fluttery dovelike coo. "Rhymes with *Go catch a hog*, or *Let's breathe some smog*." This always brought more laughs, but Cathy had never given credit to Violet, whose rhymes they were.

"Was Cathy really a counselor at this camp, Channing?" somebody would demand, laughing.

Cathy would preen before them, her green eyes glittering, her ivory complexion and shimmering hair and perfect figure all glowing.

"A brief lapse in intelligence," Channing would agree.

Cathy would start everybody laughing, but the beautiful couple never stayed long. Cathy loved the way Channing always left a room swiftly, while he and she were still the center of attention, as if they were far too busy to spend more than a few minutes in any one place.

Until October twenty-third.

On October twenty-third, Cathy Coatsworth had found herself in a police station. Her parents were there, and her brother and sister, and a lawyer.

Cathy was not speaking because she could not stop sobbing. Her family was not speaking because they were so shocked. The lawyer was not speaking because he felt silence was safer.

Cathy's family could not even look at Cathy. Their daughter? Their sister? Mixed up in drug deals?

"But I wasn't," said Cathy despairingly. "I didn't even know. I was just—just there."

The police, of course, stared at Cathy. The way men and boys always stared at Cathy. They took in the hair, golden as shining sunsets. They stared at the lovely voluptuous figure, the perfect tan, the huge brilliant green eyes. The perfect face, white teeth, sexy smile, and sensuous walk.

Cathy thought, they're not looking at me, Cathy Coatsworth. They're looking at the parts: like options on an expensive car. *Hey, look at it shine. I wouldn't mind polishing that one.*

Channing, however, had had plenty to say. It was as if, having been caught, he now found it necessary to produce details so that he would be admired for brilliance of planning. Channing's lawyer also advised silence, but Channing had never been able to bear silence.

"And what about Miss Coatsworth?" a police officer had asked Channing.

Cathy had never been referred to as Miss Coatsworth. It sounded as if she had become scum, and the officer had to distance himself from her. She would never again be called Cathy, because it was too affectionate.

"Who cares about her?" said Channing to the officer. "I only had her there because she's so gorgeous. People stare. Men leer. And Cathy is the most conceited girl on earth. She's always playing to an audience. If people don't stare, then she knocks herself out until they do. All Cathy was was good camouflage."

Cathy had reached for a chair, trying to sit before her body turned to jelly and she disgraced herself. But there were no chairs, and nobody offered to get her one. They merely looked at her in contempt. Her own parents. Her own brother. Her own sister. Their faces were identical, as if the curled lip and disgusted frown were drawn by the same cartoonist.

Channing added, "So, while they soaked up Cathy, I'd do the drug deal. She's not an accessory crimewise. She was an accessory like a piece of jewelry is. I'd just hang her out front and nobody would notice what I was doing." Channing laughed. "Especially Cathy wouldn't notice. She only notices herself, anyway."

Channing's contempt was even greater than that of her family, or the police. For Channing—whom she had adored—Cathy had been a float in a parade. All that wonderful social life: those people had been buyers, and she had been there to distract attention, so that strangers would not notice Channing's deals in the filth.

October twenty-third.

Her involvement with the police had not been for much more than just that one day. Channing had been so ready to talk that the police limited their interrogation of Cathy. They came a couple of times to the house, but she could add nothing to what they'd already learned. For Channing was right; she had noticed only herself, and never the people to whom she played.

It's one thing to know you've done something wrong. To see that your attractive little personality has a smudge.

It's quite another to know that you're the wrong kind of person altogether: that you're nothing but one big smudge.

Cathy's parents were not speaking to her.

Cathy's older sister was not speaking to her.

Cathy's younger brother and grandparents were not speaking to her.

I'm not even speaking to myself, thought Cathy.

It was true. She fixed her mind on things like which shoes to wear: the dark gray flats with the tiny black ribbon woven through the leather, or the lighter gray shoes with the more rounded toe. Cathy found if you tried hard enough, you could skip thinking altogether.

You couldn't escape at night, though.

There was something about the darkness that brought dreadful thoughts like little toads hopping onto the bed with you, their nasty warty green fingers gripping your skin, peeling it back, oozing into your brain.

Cathy slept with the lights on.

It was now November twenty-first, and Cathy had not yet figured out how to dress, or do her hair, or even walk.

Every time she flung back her hair—the thick golden glistening hair she was so proud of—she thought of Channing using that pose. Every time she pulled jeans over her long slim legs she thought of how she used to walk. Slowly, teasingly, trying to get the most attention from the most members of the opposite sex.

I'm not a person, thought Cathy. I'm an accessory.

She couldn't quite throw away her actual accessories, but she couldn't look at them, either. Not just the word, but also the ornaments offended her. She packed them all away in boxes: the belts, the earrings, the scarves, the purse collection, the sunglasses in all shades and shapes. Without them, the bedroom was bare and temporary. She felt bare when she left the house. She who had always cared so intensely about fashion and figure and face now appeared only as a stripped-down model.

A car without accessories, Cathy thought. You see me here, nothing but four wheels and an engine. No radio, no air conditioning, no speed control.

She could hardly fill her time anymore. When you didn't spend the evening planning what to wear the next day, and spend the next day shopping for what to wear the following day, what did you do? When you used to spend a happy hour trying on different belts and sashes and scarves and socks—and now you were the stripped-down model—what happened during that hour?

Nothing that Cathy could find.

She was not bored, exactly. She was stunned. Vacant. But it was not surprising to be vacant.

Men still stared at her. In a way it was gratifying. It proved she certainly did not need the accessories to be beautiful and appealing. But it proved something else, something terrible. She herself would always be just an accessory.

Then the invitation to the camp reunion arrived.

She had read it and folded it and wrinkled it up by spindling it with her fingernails (nails with no polish for the first time since she was eleven.) It always said the same thing, announced in big cheery script. Camp Menunkechogue had a reunion every five years and all former camp counselors and campers were welcome to come to the Hilton on the afternoon of Saturday, November twenty-ninth.

They have my name down on their mailing list only because Charles wrote a computer program and forgot to take me off, thought Cathy. I'm not really welcome. Nobody liked me. I was mean to Marissa. I called her Melissa on purpose. And when Marissa got all earnest, at her most camp counselor-y, I'd coo to the boys, "Isn't she cute?" I could always make them laugh at Marissa. I could even make Sin laugh at her—when I knew she had a crush on him. . . . And Violet. Little, fluffy, dopey Vi. I was furious when Jamie fell for her. . . . And of course I couldn't be bothered to make the effort to learn the little campers' names. I would write to Channing and call them "the campies." It didn't bother me at all to mix up JoAnne and Roxanne . . . but I bet it bothered JoAnne and Roxanne.

Cathy tortured herself by the hour about her behavior at camp. Once she even got out her Camp Men T-shirt and wore it around the house, to remind herself that she was probably the least kind counselor any little girl in Maine ever suffered.

I want to be like Marissa, thought Cathy. Or even like Vi.

It seemed to Cathy that Marissa and Vi were from another era: a better, finer time, where

18

personalities were unstained and kindness was unending.

One of Vi's campers had wet the bed. Cathy could not even bear to be near Laury, it was so disgusting that a twelve-year-old girl would do that. Vi had never once referred to it. Not in front of little Laury, not in front of the rest of the campers. Vi had just held her breath and dragged Laury's mattress outside to air. Laury had worshipped Vi. Cathy, as dance instructor, had wanted all the little girls to worship *her*. She'd resented Laury's dumb adoration of dumb old Violet.

I was jealous of a little girl's love, thought Cathy, wishing that she, like Channing, were facing a jail sentence. At least if you went to jail, you paid your debt to society. How was she ever going to pay her debt to Laury?

Cathy shuddered remembering the time when, during a dance practice, she had made Laury dance alone in front of twenty other girls. And then Cathy had said cruelly, "Laury, what is this perfume you're treating us to? My dear, you smell like an outhouse." Laury had frozen middance, mouth open, ankle dangling. Cathy had taunted her, "Can you last through the dance, Laury?" Laury had hunched down, trying to grow younger and smaller. And Cathy had laughed at her. Cathy had an infectious laugh; she was proud of her laugh. Cathy's laugh had leadership—when Cathy laughed, people joined in.

So all twenty girls had laughed at Laury.

Cathy tried to remember the last time she had been nice. It was a long time ago: elementary school. There was a girl named Monnie, and Cathy let Monnie sit next to her even though Monnie was a dope.

That was me at my best, thought Cathy, sobbing in her room. *Letting* a girl sit next to me. The *honor* of sitting next to me was me being nice.

Cathy had been invited to the reunion. She could go, just like anybody else.

It was being held at the Hilton, a huge, anonymous, splashy hotel. If the reunion was too terrible, she could always vanish into another dining room or another meeting room, or even take a taxi and come home early.

If it were wonderful however . . .

That was ridiculous. It could not be wonderful. Cathy doubted that anything in her life would be wonderful again. She was not a good person. Why would Vi and Marissa even speak to her?

Cathy dried her tears with her Camp Men T-shirt.

Oh, they'd speak to her all right.

Vi and Marissa were courteous. And they'd remember their little Camp Men pledge, the one Cathy had considered too silly to repeat at flag-lowering ceremonies by the lake. *I promise to be a friend to people around me and to the earth. I promise to love the world and all her glories. I promise to encourage, to praise, and to be patient. To let the world know I am a Camp Menunkechogue girl.*

Cathy wet her lips, and the creased invitation she held in her hand quivered. It seemed to her that if she could spend even one afternoon with good people, she could catch hold of their goodness. Even a straw, a splinter, of goodness would be better than this nothingness that gripped her now. Maybe some of the terrible warty green toads of the night would leave her alone if she could just see Marissa and Vi, and memorize them, and imitate them.

3

Claudia did not reply to the invitation even though it had included an RSVP.

She knew this was bad manners, but how were you supposed to make up your mind on that sort of thing until the very last minute? Claudia felt you should be able to RSVP at the door.

For the first eleven years, Claudia's life was perfect. She had not really noticed her life; she just sailed along enjoying everything from spelling to blue jeans, from her cousins to her haircuts.

And then Daddy—perfect Daddy—came home to say he was tired of being married to Mommy and was going to marry Heather Anne. Claudia would always remember how her parents ceased to be Mommy and Daddy that afternoon, and by nightfall, had become Mommy and "him." Neither Claudia nor her mother could bring themselves to use the word *Daddy* at all, so they rearranged their sentences. *"He* says . . ." *"He* lied again . . ." "Did you talk to *him*?"

And then Daddy's partner at work, Jonathan, was suddenly comforting Mommy quite a lot. Jonathan and Mommy had taken Claudia out to dinner once, both of them giggling. There was something disgusting and untrustworthy about grown-ups giggling. And sure enough, sitting by candlelight at the Chateau Rose, Mommy leaned over the plates of salad—Claudia was busy picking out the inedible parts, like mushrooms—and said it was all for the best, wasn't it, Claudia, darling? Every cloud had a silver lining and things worked out in the end, because Mommy was going to marry Jonathan now and they would all live happily ever after.

Claudia certainly doubted *that* conclusion.

Now there were two men Claudia could not call by name, and now the sentences really got complex, and required a lot of hand gestures so that the listener could guess which "he" was being referred to—her father or Jonathan.

She staggered through the winter of sixth grade. Teachers still gave arithmetic quizzes, and pencils still got blunt; she still sang soprano in the spring concert, and the Memorial Day parade arrived right on time.

About then had come the announcement that Claudia was to spend the whole summer at some wilderness camp in Maine. She could not believe they were serious. Bugs and creepy noises? Wet feet on cold days? Nasty strange girls singing stupid songs?

Summer was the good time. She would swim at the country club, play tennis with her girlfriends, ride her bike all over, and swing in the hammock, reading good books. (Bad books she would hurl across the lawn like Frisbees, which made returning them to the library tricky, but now that Jonathan had taken over library fines, Claudia liked to run them up wherever possible.)

Summer was a time to daydream and wander in hot long days, where the hours stretched, your tan deepened, and your friends waited for you on the porch.

"Camp?" Claudia had said. "What—are you kidding me?"

It seemed that this was Heather Anne's first marriage, and of course she had a right to a huge splashy wedding, which could not possibly be put together before September and would take up ever so much time. Claudia would be happier out of the way.

It seemed that Jonathan and Mommy also wanted a large wedding, and this, too, would take weeks to plan, and Claudia would be happier out of their way as well.

"What you're saying is, you guys want to ship me off so you can have fun," accused Claudia.

Of course not, said the four grown-ups, wherever did you get such an idea?

Heather Anne cajoled her to behave by showing her the lovely pale lavender satin gown Claudia would wear at their wedding. Claudia said purple was a low-class color and nobody with taste would choose that for a wedding.

Mommy and Jonathan told her she could pick her own color gown for their wedding. Claudia said she would wear black, to symbolize the mourning she would be in for her real family.

"I'll write to you all summer long," promised her mother.

"I won't write back," promised Claudia.

"Now, Claudia," said her father, "why can't you behave sensibly?"

Sensible meant that she should make things easy for them. Well, Claudia hated them all, and she could not believe she had to go to this Camp Menunke-something that you couldn't even pronounce, with all the weirdo mill-nerds that would undoubtedly like such a dump.

"What's a mill-nerd?" her father had asked.

"A nerd times a million," said Claudia. "Like you."

But when they arrived at camp, having driven past a billion pine trees to get there, Claudia's rage collapsed. She was afraid and desperate. They would go and get married and start new homes and leave her here because she'd been so mean to them, and she would never again have even half a family.

Her father and Heather Anne drove away. Claudia was left in the clutches of a counselor named Violet, who bore a sickening resemblance to Heather Anne: all fluff and yellow. But when Vi hauled her up a path so steep that Claudia said they should install chair lifts, Vi laughed so hard she almost fell off the cliff. In the tiny brown-shingled cabin were eight bunks; narrow hard bunks on which you unrolled your sleeping bag and stuck your pillow. Vi had brought designer sheets and monogrammed pink cotton blankets. Claudia met Janey and Laury right away and the three girls had sat cross-legged on Vi's designer sheets and Vi had taught them how to apply liquid eyeliner and then they had all done their nails and Claudia chose purple with gold flecks. By supper they were best friends.

Claudia could not get over how quickly you made friends at camp. Back home she'd had lots of friends, but they hadn't meant as much. The intimacy of eight girls and a crazy counselor in one tiny room, overflowing with sneakers, teddy bears, wet bathing suits, postcards from home, cassettes, nature notebooks, and crafts projects had been a wonderful thing.

Claudia had never written home. Each week you had to submit a letter before supper to show you were communicating, and Claudia had mailed empty envelopes. Vi had never told on her, and at least her parents knew she was alive, because the envelopes had been addressed in Claudia's handwriting.

The summer was wonderful.

How excruciatingly painful it had been to say good-bye to her cabinmates, her fellow campers, and Vi and Marissa. She hurt all over, and had wept in the car as they drove through Maine, and reached Massachusetts, and hurtled down the Connecticut Turnpike toward home.

In one week, school started.

A week after that, her father and Heather Anne

married, and Claudia was a bridesmaid in pale lavender satin.

Three weeks later, her mother and Jonathan married, and Claudia was a bridesmaid in lemon yellow.

It had been like having convulsions. Claudia's body jerked from one huge event to another. Claudia forgot camp. It vanished as if it had never been.

In the midst of all this came her thirteenth birthday. The four adults had gotten together in civilized terms to throw her an enormous party. They invited everybody Claudia had ever spoken to. Along with cake and favors and barbecue, there was a clown, a magician, a band, and a tethered hot-air balloon so everybody could take safe little rides. Everybody said it was the best birthday party they had ever come to.

The only thing Claudia could say about it was that she sure felt older. Thirteen was immeasurably older than twelve. At twelve you still thought wishes and tantrums could change the course of events.

Junior high was good because it was big. Five elementary schools fed into it, and Claudia was absorbed into the fabric of junior high—just another thread. But her two new families . . . she was not part of either one. School was safe. Home was sad.

When the invitation to the camp reunion arrived, Claudia was spending the weekend with her father and Heather Anne. Claudia did not enjoy weekends with them. But it was worse staying with Mommy and Jonathan, who loved being by themselves, and whose faces would crumple in disappointment if Claudia said the awful words, "I'm staying with you."

The four grown-ups had asked her opinion, of course, before setting up the stay-with-which-parent-when arrangement. They didn't want to leave her out of anything, they explained. Claudia informed them that they had left her totally out of the only thing she wanted (her original family), and that they could set up any goddamn schedule they wanted.

Never had Claudia uttered a swear word to her parents, and only a half dozen times in her life had she said the word at all. The four parents told each other it was junior high, having a bad influence on her; seventh-graders were known for their un-civilized behavior.

"It's you," cried Claudia, "who are uncivilized. What about your marriage vows, Mommy? What about yours, Daddy? Broken, all of them. I call that uncivilized. What example do you think *you* are setting?"

Claudia became expert at this. Her timing was good, too. She didn't toss off these remarks when people were busy doing the dishes or figuring their income tax. She made sure there were other adults around to increase the embarrassment, to make her parents pay.

Once her mother broke down. "Don't you care if I'm happy or not?" she wept.

"No," said Claudia, quite surprised that her mother had not yet caught on.

Claudia fingered the invitation. Printed on a computer with advanced graphics. Charles was in love with computers. Claudia leaned back against the pillows piled on this bed (all her friends told her that at least she got two bedrooms out of the remarriages; Claudia didn't see what the big deal was in that; all it meant was that anything you wanted was always in the other house).

She examined the invitation only to find a second one tucked inside—to the wedding of Charles and Alicia! Claudia was amazed. She did not have a high opinion of weddings and she was sorry that anyone as terrific as Alicia, the camp nurse, was having one.

From the kitchen her stepmother's high airy voice floated. "Claudia, dear! Claudia, honey!"

Claudia stuck her invitations under the pillows. She was certainly not going to risk sharing them with Heather Anne.

"Dinner!" called Heather Anne. "Wash your hands!"

I'm a baby? thought Claudia. Or a disgusting dweeb of a junior-high boy? I have to be *told* to be clean?

Claudia washed ferociously, turning her hands pruney, splashing water and soap all over her bathroom and leaving the wet towel on the floor. She entered the dining room like a messenger entering the enemy camp. It was definitely Heather Anne's room. White lace hung over a deep pink tablecloth. Pink scented candles in silver sticks had been lit. The roses her father had brought Heather Anne yesterday were still fresh in their crystal vase. The room was one, big, pink, silver, and crystal wedding-present collection.

Claudia ignored everything her father and Heather Anne said to her. She thought of Alicia. Last summer, Alicia had taped Claudia's sprained ankle, and rubbed soothing medication into her sunburn, and was the only person who was kind when, on a camping trip, Claudia went into the trees to go to the bathroom, and picked leaves for paper and the leaves turned out to be poison ivy. "You are the only girl in the history of Camp Men with carnal knowledge of poison ivy," said Alicia, comforting Claudia in her itchy agony. "What's carnal knowledge?" Claudia had said, and Alicia, being a nurse, gave the most intensive sex education lecture Claudia was ever to receive in her life.

Claudia had known what sex was, of course, but not quite so graphically, not with such a wealth of detail. It was really disgusting to picture Daddy and Heather Anne, or Mommy and Jonathan doing that. It made you positively prefer poison ivy.

At the dinner table Claudia thought, Ick. Alicia is going to do that with Charles? Ick. And Charles is so old!

Heather Anne had made coleslaw. Claudia hated mayonnaise and hated cabbage and had told Heather Anne a hundred times. And the steak was rare. Practically bloody. Claudia felt sick even looking at raw meat.

Back when her *real* family existed, there had

31

been no Heather Anne to serve disgusting food. But it was no use changing houses. Claudia's own mother no longer served good, comforting, dull stuff. Like Kraft Macaroni and Cheese, or instant mashed potatoes. "Jonathan doesn't like that," Mommy would say, serving some horrid crunchy thing with wormy-looking Japanese vegetables.

It seemed to Claudia that the last good thing in her life was Camp Menunkechogue and the last two people who truly loved her were her counselor, Vi, and her camp nurse, Alicia.

"Now, Claudia," said her father. "Some dear old friends of Heather Anne's are going to be in town the weekend of November twenty-ninth. The Saturday after Thanksgiving. That's your weekend with us, but you can stay with Mommy and Jonathan, can't you." He put no question mark in his sentence. He was telling her.

"Why?" said Claudia. "You don't want to introduce me to Heather Anne's dear old friends?"

"Claudia, don't be rude."

You're the rude ones, thought Claudia. Always shipping me off. A few months ago she would have screamed at them. Tonight she let it pass. She had another roll, since there was nothing else edible. Wait. The Saturday after Thanksgiving Mommy and Jonathan were having a big cocktail party, which they had planned for that date because she was to be here, with Daddy and Heather Anne. "Oh—but—"

"But what?" said Heather Anne.

"Nothing." Claudia finished her roll. Nobody

wants me, she thought. Some Thanksgiving it will be. Two days later I'm an abandoned kid.

Heather Anne yelled at her for not eating any protein. Her father yelled at her for not cooperating. Claudia didn't cry, didn't break the wedding presents or start a food fight. She went back up to her room and stared at her homework. It blurred before her eyes. She leaned against the pillows and heard something crunch. She fished the reunion invitation out, smoothed away the wrinkles and reread it. It was also for the Saturday after Thanksgiving.

I'll just go, thought Claudia. Why tell anybody? I won't be at anybody's house, and I bet none of them will even notice. I'll spend the night with somebody they've never even heard of, and maybe I won't even come back at all.

So there.

4

___

Marissa had a date for the wedding.

Normal teenagers went to the movies on their first date. Or to McDonald's for french fries. Or to Friendly's for ice cream. But no, Marissa's first date with Sinclair Franklin was to a wedding.

What would it be like, sitting together while Alicia and Charles took their marriage vows? Would Sin murmur to her, "Boy, you'll never catch me saying that!" Or would he whisper, "Gosh, Mariss—kind of makes you dream, doesn't it?"

Marissa had had a crush on Sin since last spring, when they'd found out they were going to be counselors together at Camp Men. The crush had become a burden, the sort only Sin's wide shoulders could carry, but Sin had no crush at all. He liked Marissa and that was it. They talked easily on the phone now, because they'd both been campers themselves at Camp Men for years and then counselors and so they had a thousand memories in common.

But while Marissa could recall every syllable of every conversation, Sin was more likely to forget he had ever spoken to her, and his side of the conversation was usually a rerun of what he had said the last time.

But this time—this sacred time!—Sin had said on the phone, "Say, Mariss. Want to go to the wedding with me?" Sin's voice was cheerful and rather bouncy. It didn't suit his looks, which were strong and solid. Sin was shaped like a triangle, with extremely wide shoulders, as if he had come into the world prepadded for football, and from there he dwindled into slim waist and narrow hips. Sin's clothes never quite fit because all the fabric needed at the shoulders just dangled around the rest of him.

"Sure," Marissa had said casually, although it was the most exciting invitation of her love life.

"Okay," Sin had said, as if they were ordering groceries. "Now let's match. I'll feel better if we match. What're you wearing?"

"I haven't decided yet."

"I'm wearing a suit," Sin had proclaimed, as if this were so extraordinary he didn't want her to faint when she saw him. "With a vest. It's very dark gray, and you can just barely make out the plaid, because it's so sophisticated, and cream-colored, button-down-collar oxford shirt, and a very dark red tie. I look great."

Marissa was sure of that.

Sin had said, "So you think gray and cream and dark red, Marissa?"

Marissa had assured him she thought this quite often.

When she got off the phone she told her mother, and her mother said, "I suppose you think I'm going to take you shopping until we find a suitable wedding-guest outfit in that color combination? I suppose you think we're just going to ignore that lovely dark blue wool paisley and forget about the skirt and sweater your grandmother got you, and pretend you don't own the striped—" Her mother sighed. Her mother made threatening gestures toward the checkbook and purse. Then she laughed. "Actually, I like Sin, too," she confided. "We'd better get started. What store shall we hit first?"

Gray and cream and dark red ruled their lives. It was the old story: the moment you've decided on a color combination, it goes out of fashion and nobody stocks it.

Marissa and her mother went shopping every day after school and found nothing except dull matronly clothes for which Marissa would have had to gain fifty pounds and dye her hair gray to look right in. "I don't know why we're going through all this torment for Sin," complained her mother. "We could just as easily go through it all for Heath. Why don't you call Heath and see what he's wearing? Maybe you could match him more easily."

All the girls at Camp Men had adored Heath. Dark and romantic, with a family fraught with sad secrets—who could ask for anything more? Heath

37

Hesper had been an excellent camp counselor. Hurling his intense energy into making camp the perfect place on earth for little boys, Heath had hung on to his sanity. He told nobody about himself, earning from Violet the nickname Dark, as in "I'm in the dark about you, Heath." They all made up stories about Heath. None of them was even remotely right. For it wasn't Heath's story at all that mattered; it was his father's. Heath couldn't even have his own tragedy. He was whipped by somebody else's.

In the last few moments at camp, while everyone was saying their tearful farewells, Heath had said, in their presence, "I'll call you, Marissa." And then he had hugged her, hard, and kissed her, harder.

Naturally everybody drew conclusions from this.

She and Heath would begin dating and her social life would be perfect. Camp was in northern Maine, but home to most of the campers and counselors was in Westchester County and New York City. Marissa had planned joyously for dates: how she would go into Manhattan on the train and have dinner with Heath, and how Heath would come up to Rye to see her, and go to the high-school dances.

It turned out, however, that when Heath had said "call," he'd meant "call." As in phone. He had a hundred problems and he wanted to air them with Marissa. By phone.

His problems were impressive by any standards, including the standards of the *New York Times*, the *Washington Post*, and ABC, NBC, and CBS, but

Marissa was crushed. How she blushed when she remembered her fantasies. And her mother was amused. Marissa hated that more than anything— her mother laughing slightly on Mondays when Heath called. Marissa hated, hated, hated being laughed at.

Mondays were hardest for him: he had the break of the weekend to hibernate in his apartment and pretend that what was happening wasn't. Then when school started, he had to face once more his friends and enemies. His father's trial was getting very heavy media coverage. Headlines said, WALL STREET RIPOFF ARTIST NOW ADMITS TO MORE THAN 20 MIL. And there was HESPER TESTIFIES IT WAS FUN. Another nice one was HESPER FAMILY RICH FOREVER ON TRICK TRADES.

On Mondays Heath would call Marissa to tell her in detail how he was feeling and how rotten it was. She became Heath's safety valve. But I'm just sixteen! thought Marissa. I don't want to be your shrink. I want to be your girlfriend!

Heath didn't want to hold her hand or kiss her lips. She was Clorox to pour on the dirty laundry of his troubles, and maybe he would feel cleaner after he talked to her.

As for the kiss and hug, Marissa knew now that Heath had just been afraid to go home. The protection and the isolation of camp had ended. All that kiss had done was extend his safety zone a minute.

Last Monday when Heath called, Marissa had been lying on the floor of her bedroom with her feet up on the bed, staring at a poster of Billy Idol and thinking that, of her own two idols, Heath and Sin, emotion ran depressingly one way.

Did they idolize her? No.

Did they ask her out? No.

Did they ask what *she* was wearing, so they could match *her*? No.

Did they ever do anything but telephone? No.

She could not say one more time, "Poor Heath," or "Oh, Heath, I'm so sorry, that's so awful." She could not even manage, "Mmmmmmm."

"Oh, God, Mariss," said Heath from Manhattan, "and my father's putting on weight. He eats when he's nervous. He's not just going to be a crook, he's going to be a *fat* crook."

Marissa began having a tantrum alone in her own room. She drummed her feet violently against the sideboards of her bed. The bed began inching across the room as she attacked it, and she had to scoot along on her back to catch up with it and drum some more. "Heath!" she screamed. "Who *cares*? Noboby cares! Do you hear me? This is boring!"

There was no sound except the sound of her shoes whacking the sideboards. Heath finally mumbled, "I—I wouldn't have bothered you—I thought—well—"

"Talk about something real," shrieked Marissa. "Tell me about class. What you wore. How the team did. Whether you're renting a movie for the VCR tonight. *Stop telling me about your father's trial!*"

Her voice echoed in the phone and around her room. The bed was out of reach. She was off the rug and onto the dust kittens that had moments ago been hidden by the bed. This is one of my best friends on the phone, thought Marissa. What I just said to him was awful.

She tried to think of an apology, and then became enraged all over again. Why should *she* apologize? It was Heath's fault, he was so self-centered. She didn't care how hard his life was; she was much more interested in how hard *her* life was.

In Manhattan, Heath took a deep breath.

In Rye, Marissa slammed the phone down. Clouds of dust kittens danced around the shivering cord.

For quite a while she lay on the floor, wanting to call Heath back and never wanting to call him back. Hoping he would call her and hoping he would never call her. She was still lying there when the phone rang and it was Sin, to say his dad was letting him take the good car, and he could drive Marissa to the Hilton, and was she spending the night at the hotel?

"Yes, I'm staying over. The wedding's at eight, and I doubt if the reception will be over till long after midnight, and I want to stay up all night anyhow talking to Vi." If Vi's coming, thought Marissa. If she wants to talk to me, too.

They discussed gray and cream and dark red and who else would be there and wouldn't it be great to see everybody again. "Heath call you yet tonight?" Sin asked, because he knew his Mondays. Sin liked to be kept up to date on Heath's situation.

Marissa had promised Heath she would never

tell any details of his problems. But her crush on Sin was so great that she offered the news so that Sin would keep calling.

I am scum, thought Marissa. The bottom of a stagnant pond. Algae growing on my moral values. Oil slicks on my friendships.

I, Marissa, who prided myself on being the best possible counselor, the girl on whom they could all model themselves—clean, honest, true, dependable, generous, kind, and courteous—I am the one who passes on gossip and abandons a friend in need.

Marissa skipped Sin's question about Heath calling and described the outfit she and her mother had finally found. Sin thought it sounded perfect. "You'll be beautiful, Mariss," he said affectionately. "You and I will look terrific together."

But it was not balm to her soul. Her soul felt too lousy for mere balm. It needed major surgery.

She wished she could talk to Violet about it. But she had neither written to Vi nor phoned her, not once since camp ended. They had hugged goodbye so intensely! Promised to be forever friends, saying this as one word—inextricably entwined: *foreverfriends*.

And they had not communicated once.

Was it that camp was so precious it had to remain enclosed in its summer time-space?

Or had they known in their hearts they were not foreverfriends but only summer friends?

Marissa yearned for Vi, silly frothy Vi, with her hot rollers and her cases of eye makeup and her frilly clothes for any occasion, even though the only occasion had been campfire. And yet she dreaded Vi. Was Vi, away from camp, sort of embarrassing? Would Vi's chatter, so comical and endearing at camp, be blather elsewhere?

What if they hugged hello—and they were strangers?

Marissa had never been to any kind of reunion. When you first thought of it, it was the warmest image possible. All hugs and laughter, joy and pleasure.

Then loopholes pierced the dream. There might be nothing to talk about. They might have nothing in common but hanging up their regulation blue tank suits to dry, or smushing down their graham crackers to make S'mores.

She thought of calling Vi quickly, before the reunion. But you couldn't just phone a person you had ignored for three months.

What if the other girls had been in touch all along? What if Violet had written to the others, and gone to parties with them, and been on the phone with them? What if Vi's mailbox had been full of letters from buddies at camp, while nobody had even considered writing to Marissa?

And what—worst of all—if she did not matter even to Sin? Perhaps Marissa was Sin's shield. He could not very well wear his trademark wraparound sunglasses at the wedding, so he would wear Marissa. Sin's crush had been on Cathy, who had ignored Sin all summer in favor of Trevor and Brandon. Sin had followed Cathy like a puppy, hoping for anything, even a kick, that would show Cathy'd noticed him. He got the kick on the last day, when Cathy turned out to have a serious boyfriend from home she had never gotten around to mentioning.

Perhaps Sin was afraid to face Cathy, and that was his only reason for wanting to match Marissa and go together.

Marissa decided not to go. She couldn't face Cathy, either. Cathy possessed a beauty so demanding you could not stop staring. It hooked you, with barbs. And then Cathy would humiliate you, and people laughed at you, and you crumbled in public.

I could call Heath back, Marissa thought. But Heath—even if he accepted her apologies—had lost any ability to have fun. Marissa wanted to be with Sin, who considered it his duty in life to have fun.

She had spent her summer engineering other people's fun, and this had been fine, because that was what camp counselors did. But it was not fair to continue it in the fall.

Oh, what will I do? thought Marissa miserably. How am I going to face all these people? I'm not the girl I pretended to be at camp. I'm not good and sweet and perfect. I can't even write my best girlfriend or be kind to my second-best boyfriend.

But then she remembered that Cathy despised them all and laughed at the idea of camp. Cathy would never come.

With that burden gone, Marissa could breathe again and, just a little bit, began to get excited about going to the reunion after all.

5

Claudia's plans took shape.

If she were to be gone for a weekend, and neither parent know, she had to have places to stay at night. Claudia had no interest in park benches in the winter. She got her best friend, Lynn, to invite her to stay at her house on Friday night. That was good because Lynn's house was near the center of town and the railroad station, and Lynn's parents always slept till noon on Saturday. They would never know that instead of being driven home by a parent, Claudia had walked downtown to take a train alone.

Saturday she would be going to the Hilton for the reunion, and since the wedding itself was in the evening, with a reception afterward, it would end very late. It was reasonable, therefore, to spend Saturday night at the Hilton.

Claudia got the phone number of the hotel from

the operator. In her deepest, most mature voice, she called to make a room reservation. Claudia had never been so proud of herself. She requested a single room for the night for Miss Claudia Goodman, and the voice replied, "Certainly, madam."

Claudia loved that. *Madam*. And her parents didn't even know! She hugged it to herself. A secret revenge. All the little games they had played on her—and now she could play a few moves on them. She liked being the only one to know. It gave her quite a feeling of superiority. She—their thirteen-year-old child—would be on her own in another town for two days and a night and they would never even know. They, who prided themselves on being the perfect parents.

She packed her suitcase carefully. For the reunion itself she would wear her favorite torn jeans, her old sneakers, and her beloved Camp Men sweatshirt, faded now from many washings. For the wedding, the bridesmaid dress from her mother's wedding. This was a floor-length lemon yellow satin with many ruffles and bows and a long sash, with an overlay of ivory lace like a Victorian apron. It swished and whispered when she moved.

She added food. It might be a Hilton hotel, but you always needed your own food supply. She had learned that at camp. Claudia put in Mallomars, Cheetos, and Oreos. That should last for a night. She would stay awake all night watching forbidden movies on TV and eating cookies in bed and laughing because Daddy and Heather Anne and Mommy and Jonathan wouldn't even know.

And if they should find out, by some chance, and suddenly realize at dawn that none of them had Claudia, well, that would be rather pleasant, too. Claudia did not mind at all if they panicked and called the FBI and got ready to pay ransoms.

When she arrived at Lynn's house, Lynn's mother burst out laughing. "Why, Claudia Goodman, that's the largest *overnight* bag I've ever seen in my life. How long are you planning to stay with us? Two years?"

Claudia managed to smile politely.

Upstairs Lynn opened the suitcase and began rifling through it. "Oooooh, look! It's your bridesmaid dress! Are we going to play dress-up? Oooooh, neat!"

Claudia liked to think she had left such childish games behind. But she didn't want to explain anything to Lynn, so she said Lynn could put the dress on. After a huge supper of leftover turkey and stuffing, cranberry sauce, and gravy, the girls went back upstairs so Lynn could practice being a bridesmaid. "Whose house were you at for Thanksgiving?" asked Lynn, who found divorce very exciting.

"Both. I stayed at Daddy's on Wednesday. Then we all went to a restaurant on Thursday, and I went back to Mommy's after," said Claudia. She hated admitting she'd eaten Thanksgiving dinner in a restaurant. It was saying out loud, *we are not a family, we are people who eat out on holidays*. But Lynn was filled with envy, and it is always nice to be envied, so Claudia made up lots of details about how terrific the restaurant was.

First thing in the morning Claudia was up and into her jeans and sweatshirt (so large it reached her knees) and packing her suitcase.

"You're not walking?" said Lynn, when Claudia prepared to leave. "Claudia, you live miles from here. Wait till noon and Mom will be up to drive you."

Claudia insisted on leaving.

"Are you mad at me?" said Lynn anxiously.

"No, I have a train to catch."

Now Lynn was really impressed. She put on her coat and helped Claudia pull the suitcase. It had two tiny wheels at one end and a stiff handle at the other. It was like yanking a dog along on a very short leash.

The weather was very cold. Claudia zipped up her ski jacket, festooned with last year's chair lift tickets. She had forgotten mittens and scarf. She shivered.

"Where's the train to?" asked Lynn as they waited on the platform.

Claudia thought. "Boston," she said finally.

"Oh, my goodness! Who are you going to see? Relatives? New ones you got with Heather Anne or Jonathan?"

Claudia was grateful for this suggestion. "Yes. Heather Anne's sister—um—Vivian—is having me for a while. Vivian is—um—a vet, and I can play with all her dogs. And ponies."

"Wow," said Lynn. "And you're going to Boston on the train all by yourself?"

"Sure."

Lynn was not allowed to go to the YWCA to

swim by herself, let alone Boston by train. Claudia waved good-bye to Lynn, being relaxed and superior, although she had only been on a train twice herself, as whenever the Goodmans had gone to New York or Boston, they'd driven.

When Lynn was out of sight, the adventure began to count. Nobody knows where I am! exulted Claudia, staring out the grimy window. When the train arrived at her station, she got off, signaled a taxi, and arrived quickly at the Hilton. She was a little surprised by how much this transportation cost, but shrugged. She had fifty dollars birthday money, so there was no problem.

A gleaming maroon-and-gold doorman opened the hotel door for her. He looked like an usher at a wedding, only more colorful.

The lobby was fantastic. Claudia abandoned her suitcase for a moment just to peek around and explore. Thick vermilion carpet with gold-key trim led down corridors that stretched away like those in airline terminals. The vast lobby was divided by gleaming marble columns rising two stories, and by flower arrangements as big as pianos.

Claudia darted past a very long, wooden check-in desk, at which dozens of people were crowded, and where phones rang continually and demandingly. Beyond the ranks of elevators and small shops selling imported perfumes and newspapers, the interior of the Hilton suddenly opened up. An enormous room, as big and as high as a school gym, was crisscrossed by silver balconies hanging from silver ropes. Climbing like spider webs into the vaulted, skylit ceiling, the silver stairs seemed hung by tinsel from starry chandeliers.

Claudia was entranced.

She took the steps two at a time. A chandelier hung temptingly close to the junction of stairs and balcony. Had nobody ever swung from it? Claudia was confident she could find a Camp Men alum who would give it a try.

Claudia hopped back down the stairs and located her suitcase. It was still beside an enormous red leather sofa kind of thing—circular—with palms growing in the middle. The sofa would be useful if you had twenty friends who wanted to sit with their backs to each other.

Claudia sat for a while, watching people come and go. She was particularly taken by two, very thin, elegant ladies, each of whom had a very thin, elegant dog on a jeweled leash. Claudia preferred dogs that could knock down letter carriers.

Claudia was quite hungry. She should have had breakfast with Lynn, but she had forgotten food in the rush to be away before Lynn's parents were awake. A large, dark olive green sign said in twisted gold script that there were a total of six restaurants in the hotel, to suit any taste. Claudia wondered which one would suit a taste for Special K and bananas?

First she'd check in. Investigate her room. See if there were any of those free things she loved that her father brought back when he traveled—small packets of hand lotion or shampoo.

Claudia waited in line at the high, gleaming check-in desk, finally giving her name to the young woman at the computer terminal. The computer printed out Claudia's name on her bill. Claudia was thrilled. She had never had her very own bill before. She loved that: the officialness of being Claudia Goodman, hotel guest.

"And how are you going to pay, Miss Goodman?" said the woman.

"I have cash," Claudia said proudly.

The woman smiled. "Fine. Your room will be number eight-fifty-five, but I am afraid it's not yet vacant. You may get the key at about noon. The price of the room is one hundred seventy dollars, and you must check out before eleven tomorrow morning. We'll check your luggage for you until the room is available." She rang an old-fashioned bell, and a very old man tottered up to take Claudia's suitcase, giving her a pink plastic ticket to reclaim it.

One hundred and seventy dollars? thought Claudia. For one room? For one night?

She did not dare ask if this could be the wrong price. She could not bring herself to admit she did not have even a third of that amount.

The businessman behind Claudia sighed with impatience. The family on her right eyed her Camp Men sweatshirt with interest. The man on her left bumped her leg with his briefcase, apologized without looking at her, and hurried away. The check-in clerk waited calmly.

If she said she couldn't afford the room after all, would the clerk ask questions? Would she make Claudia phone her parents? What *was* she going to do for the night now?

Claudia was desperately afraid she was going to cry. She could just imagine the telephone call home. How they would tell her she was childish and silly, irritating and uncooperative. How they would laugh at her, and punish her. How they would tell their cocktail guests what she had tried to do. ("And can you imagine, Florence, the child actually thought she could stay at the Hilton for fifty dollars?" . . . Gales of laughter.)

Claudia's heart hurt and her chest grew tight. She remembered her excuse to Lynn. "You know what? My aunt Vivian is really going to pay for the room when she gets here. Maybe I won't check in now. When Aunt Vivian gets here, she'll do it for both of us."

The check-in clerk nodded without interest. "What's your Aunt Vivian's last name?"

"Bskxpyvk," said Claudia quickly, and she gripped her luggage ticket and fled. Luckily the lobby was jammed with people going in and out, and her flight was covered by pin-striped suits and mink coats. Claudia disappeared down a hallway. She ducked into a telephone booth to hide, but when she shut the door the light went on, so she left the door open. The inside was upholstered, like a restaurant booth.

I'm not giving up my adventure, thought Claudia. I'm not phoning home for help. I'll figure something out. And I'm not telling anybody now, because they'd find out about that awful thing at the desk. I'll never let anybody know about that.

She decided that, later on, she would use this

phone and pretend to be Aunt Vivian, canceling Claudia Goodman's reservation.

Farther down the same hall was the Country Squire, A Family-Style Café. Claudia checked out the menu. Toast, eggs, grapefruit, orange juice, and coffee were seven dollars. Oh, well, thought Claudia recklessly. She ordered the biggest breakfast on the menu.

It was ten in the morning.

The reunion began at two.

6

All right, said Cathy to herself as she got into the taxi and asked for the railroad station. I will not flirt. I will not demand attention. I will not steal the show. I will not alienate any girls. I will be nice. I will be patient and generous—

Who, me? she thought. That's like trying to take off fifty pounds in one day.

All right. I'll make two rules and stick to them. One. No flirting. Two. No grandstand shows to get attention. Or even little minor shows to get attention.

Great, thought Cathy, fishing in her purse for the taxi fare. If I don't get their attention, nobody'll speak to me. What good is it going to a reunion if nobody speaks to me?

She smoothed her dress. A plain, dark crimson wool sheath, no jewelry except small, gold hoop earrings. Touch of makeup. Flat dull shoes. Cathy had always been able to analyze her looks correctly, and she knew that, although it had been her intention to dress down, she was even more beautiful with less.

Perhaps you could climb out of bad habits. You could not climb out of your own body.

Cathy had hope—not much, but a little—for the reunion. When she'd telephoned the hotel to make her reservation, the clerk had told her that a Camp Menunkechogue party of three had booked a suite for four and needed someone to fill the fourth slot. Would she like to have it? Yes, she said quickly, hoping her roommate would be the girls with whom she could start her new personality.

But what if they knew her? Suppose one of them was Marissa? Or Vi? Those two would cancel their reservations if they found they had to share a room with Cathy Coatsworth. She'd be alone in a four-person suite.

Cathy climbed on the train and sat alone. She was alone in her heart and alone in her thoughts. The blue sky and brisk autumn wind meant nothing to her. She felt nothing, knew nothing. Except loneliness.

By noon, Claudia had checked out the British Hunt Room (oil paintings of dogs chasing foxes, thick furniture, and food that looked equally heavy). She had walked up all ten flights of stairs in the hotel, and ridden in every elevator. She had investigated the three little shops (boring) and wandered into the IBM meeting room to see if she could blend in. She could not.

She was sauntering through the front lobby for the umpteenth time when she realized that somebody was eyeing her very suspiciously. Not a uniformed bellboy or doorman, but a thin, frowning man in a fine dark suit, with a flower in his lapel. Claudia thought she had better avoid him, but he blocked her way.

"Hi, there," said Claudia sweetly. Attack is always better than defense, she reasoned. "Do you by any chance know where the Camp Menunke-chogue reunion is to be held, and could you show me the way?"

"Oh, you're here for the camp reunion." The man laughed. "Of course, I should have guessed. It's not actually scheduled till two, of course, but I believe the man in charge is setting up. Follow the silver stairs, cross the hanging balcony, and the Mayflower Room is third on your right."

Claudia bounded away, as if joining a volleyball team at camp. The man in charge, sure enough, was Charles, mixing paint.

"Charles," said Claudia severely, "this is your wedding day. Can't you think of anything better to do?"

Charles laughed. "Hello, Claudia. You're my first alum. Good to see you. Here, help the waiter with that tablecloth."

So Claudia helped with hanging vast, white linen cloths on huge tables, and unfolding chairs, and centering flowers, and rolling in moving coat racks. There is nothing like being useful to take your mind off your troubles, and Claudia momentarily forgot that she had a big problem coming that night.

She took a message from one of the hotel staff to the linen rooms, and coming back she was gratified to find four Camp Men boys on the balcony, pummeling each other, screaming, and threatening to toss each other over the side. They dared her to catch them. Claudia tossed her hair and turned away. The boys yodeled after her, and then suddenly shouted the great, all-time warning, "Counselor coming! Counselor coming!"

Vi! thought Claudia. It's got to be Vi!

Laughing, overjoyed, already running, she searched for the counselor. There, below her on the silver stairs, was the unmistakable golden head of the one counselor Claudia had truly despised.

Cathy Coatsworth.

Sin had been allowed to take his father's Jaguar, and he was so proud of himself in that terrific sports car, he could hardly see straight. He definitely could not see Marissa. He did not even notice how carefully she had picked out clothing to match his—gray and dark red and cream. Her crimson sweater perfectly set off her thick dark hair, and the deep gray skirt and cream-and-black scarf, made her feel more sophisticated than she had ever felt in her life. She did not feel like a teenager going to a camp reunion but like an adult going to her first job.

"Hi, Mriss!" said Sin. "Get this car! Fantastic, huh? Dad bought it this summer, and as long as I keep it in the hotel garage overnight, I get to use it.

I'm almost sorry we have to go to this dumb reunion. Would you rather head north and drive up to Canada? We could see how this baby does under all sorts of traffic conditions!" Sin didn't wait for her answer; he was already in the driver's seat, panting for joy.

I love this jerk? thought Marissa. Who hasn't even spotted me yet? Who wants me in the car only to appreciate his driving skills?

At least she wasn't a cover against Cathy. He might not even see Cathy against the glitter of his Jag. Though Cathy could probably outshine a whole dealership full of Jaguars if she made the effort. And Cathy would always, always, make the effort.

Marissa said, "We look perfect for the wedding, but do you think we're dressed properly for the camp reunion?"

"Aw, Marissa. We're not going to play games and do activities. It won't be camp. We'll circulate, go to the bar and the buffet, show off a little, and find out what everybody's been doing. Wonder what Heath will drive up in? Probably two or three Jaguars at once, with all that money to throw around."

"Sin! You know he hates that money. It's stolen."

"That's what he says to you, anyhow. What else is he going to say, when you think about it? He can hardly tell you he couldn't care less where it came from. He wants you on his side, and you're very moral, Marissa."

Oh, yeah, she thought. I, who tell you Heath's secrets and can't be bothered to listen to his problems, I'm very moral.

But nobody would know she wasn't. She and Sin would circulate and converse, and everybody would think that Marissa in her crimson and gray was the wholesome embodiment of Camp Menun-kechogue girls.

"If he's not driving up in a Jag, how *is* Heath getting here?" said Sin.

Marissa admitted she didn't know.

"I thought you talked to him all the time. Is he even coming at all?"

Marissa didn't know that, either.

"I guess I misjudged this," said Sin, and he actually looked at her for a moment. It's only because we're ten cars back from a red light, Marissa thought cynically. "I thought you and Heath were as close as the bark on a tree," added Sin.

Heath had thought so, too. Expected her to nurse his wounds, put Band-Aids on his cuts. Never asked for her living, breathing, visible company, though. So who was close to whom? Or was that one of the things you never knew in life?

Marissa shrugged and looked out the window. They were in a cement cavern approaching the turnpike entrance. She read the graffiti and regretted it.

"Say. Is this the Camp Men girl we all knew and loved?" teased Sin. "Sulking out the window?"

"You never knew me at all, Sinclair Franklin!" said Marissa sharply. "Or loved me, either. You didn't even notice—" She bit off her sentence. To finish it would be begging for compliments.

Sin had stopped looking at her, anyway. The

light had turned green; he was out of the traffic, surging up the entrance ramp to the turnpike, passing a station wagon, leaping between a moving van and a Datsun, getting into the third lane, and passing the speed limit, all in about sixty seconds. "What a car!" Sin murmured contentedly to himself.

Marissa sat forgotten on his right. She tried mentally to take her crush on Sin, throw it out the window, and have it be run over by all the million cars on the turnpike.

Heather Anne said to her husband, "Oh, darling, look. Claudia left her schoolbooks here at Thanksgiving. I know she has that report to write and she'll need this whole stack. Why don't you run them over to the other house."

They both hated going to the other house.

Claudia's father said, "Why don't *you* run them over, darling? I've really got so much to do."

"But my friends are due any moment, darling. I really have to be here."

Claudia's father frowned. "I'm not sure we should bail her out so frequently. She has to learn to keep track of her own possessions, and perhaps a bad grade would teach her a lesson." The thought of Claudia having a bad grade actually upset him very much. But not enough to take the books straight over to the other house.

After Heather Anne's guests arrived, and conversation slowed down, and the dear old friends ran out of things to say, he knew it was just a matter of minutes before he would take the books over after all.

It's the kind of hotel that's meant to intimidate, Vi thought, approaching the building.

Immensely high ceilings sparkled with distant chandeliers. Uniformed doormen regarded each person who approached with great contempt or with great respect.

The doorman, Violet told herself, is a stranger. I do not care in the slightest whether he treats me with respect or contempt.

This was a lie. She desperately wanted the doorman to be impressed. To treat her better than he would the common run of guests.

She was wearing the clothes of Jasmine's choice, clothes not quite right for her own petite figure. Soft black leather boots ended high under a long clingy skirt of fine black wool. Jasmine's four gold-rope necklaces rested on a long, belted Viyella shirt of a blurry dark gold, brown, and red. A thick wool scarf picked up the red and lay casually on her shoulders to set off her yellow curls. In her heart, Vi knew you needed to be five foot nine to wear the outfit. Vi was five one.

She was carrying her ski jacket because, although it was frigid out, the ski jacket was pink and looked ridiculous with the sophisticated clothes. She tried to crunch up the jacket so nobody could spot it, but the thick down stuffing spread through her fingers and oozed out like rising bread dough. The doorman smiled broadly as he held open the lobby door.

Vi stalked behind a flower arrangement so large it could have been divided among several hospitals. In the shade of gladiolus taller than she was, Vi struggled to stow the ski jacket out of sight. Hordes of beautiful people strolled by, leisurely in their wealth and style. Other beautiful people dashed about at great speed, giving off an aura of power and urgency.

Vi just knew Jamie was going to appear when she had her purse handle in her mouth and was trying to cram the ski jacket down into her makeup case.

Farther on, between Vi and the enormous reception desks, was a meeting board. Large and black, it used small white letters on black ledges to announce locations.

AMA, 3rd floor West, Shore Room
Welcome IBM! Main Lounge check-in
SUNY, info, Room 612

Nothing about Camp Menunkechogue.

Great, thought Vi. I have the wrong day.

Next to her, a group of attractive men and women, executive types carrying briefcases and wearing company name tags, burst into laughter. "How do you pronounce *that*?"

"I haven't seen a T-shirt like that since I was nine years old!"

How could she have missed it! Not content with mere black and white, Charles had brought a six-foot tall, green sandwich board. Pinned to the sides were boys' and girls' T-shirts with the camp logo on them, and in shrieking red Magic Marker, the huge words.

CAMP MENUNKECHOGUE REUNION!!!!!!
HI, GUYS!!!
WELCOME ABOARD. WEAR YOUR T-SHIRTS.
COME ONE****COME ALL!!!
MAYFLOWER ROOM 2ND FLOOR
LOTS OF GOOD GAMES AND ACTIVITIES PLANNED!!!!!

Nobody will come, thought Vi. Only little kids. Eight-year-olds. I didn't hear from anybody because nobody else would lower themselves. If they're going to the wedding, they'll show up at eight tonight, not for Charles's games and fun activities.

I was the only one stupid enough to come.

7

Alicia was alone in her room at the Hilton for the first time in days. Her mother, her friends, Charles of course, her bridesmaids, everybody involved with the details of a large wedding had hovered around, accomplishing things or getting in the way. But now she was alone.

Alicia opened the closet door at the far end of her room. It was a lovely room: the walls a sort of damask, the bedspreads something that gleamed, the mirrors bright and trimmed in gold. But she cared nothing for it. It was the closet that counted.

She took out her wedding gown. Very carefully she laid it on the bed, and then she sat next to it, and touched its soft silken fabric, and ran her fingers over the lace, and circled the hundreds of tiny, tiny pearls.

My wedding gown. My perfect day.

Charles. My husband.

She had had to take off her eye makeup because she was so happy she kept crying. This had never happened to Alicia before: tears of joy. Her eyes were puffy. She didn't even care. They would clear up by eight tonight when she appeared before her wedding guests . . . and Charles, dear Charles, stood at the far end of the aisle.

Her favorite color was pale peach and she had chosen it for her four bridesmaids, with a deeper, rosier peach for her maid of honor, and flowers in cascades—roses in the deeper color, with ferns and baby's breath and stephanotis and ribbons that would curl and hang low and dance around the girls' long dresses as they walked so slowly toward Charles.

The wedding consultant had said that peach as a color was a bit out of season, and Alicia had said it was *her* season and she would have peach if she wanted peach and that was that.

I'm getting married, thought Alicia.

It was such a lovely and perfect thought that there was room for nothing else in her mind. When her travel alarm went off, she couldn't believe it. Now she was going to have to appear at the camp reunion.

Well, Mother was right, thought Alicia. It was dumb to combine the camp reunion with the wedding. I cannot think about two things like that at one time. I will have to go downstairs to the Mayflower Room and talk with old campers about rashes and sunburns we have known, about twisted ankles I have treated, and campfire songs we have sung together.

The only togetherness I want is with Charles.

Four hours of camp reunion. Yes, Mother, you're right, we're crazy.

But, Alicia reflected, she would be crazy like this many more times in her life. Charles owned the two Menunkechogue camps: boys and girls all the way around the lovely little gem of a Maine lake. Every summer till they were old and gray (and maybe then, too), she and Charles would return to Maine to run Camp Menunkechogue for Boys and Camp Menunkechogue for Girls.

Alicia pulled on her jeans. She added a Camp Men sweatshirt. How ridiculous to be purposely putting this on only hours before her own wedding. She would have to leave the reunion early to have her hair done, and then come back to her room to slide into her wedding gown.

While she was laughing, sitting on the bed stroking her gown, Charles knocked and entered. He was wearing red shorts and a Camp Men T-shirt. He looked rather silly, as he always did when dressed like one of his campers, and yet just right, as if born to the T-shirt the way princes are born to the purple. Alicia jumped up to kiss and hug him. "I love you, Charles."

He was uncomfortable with bold declarations like that. He said, "We've got to go on down to the Mayflower Room. The kids are starting to arrive."

"You go down. I'll join you later."

"But you're all ready. Come on."

"I have to put away my gown."

"I'll wait while you hang it up."

"It takes longer than that," explained Alicia. "I have to enjoy putting it away."

Charles sighed and said okay he understood, although obviously he didn't, and he set off for the Mayflower Room. Alicia touched the gown twice more before her cousins, who were to be bridesmaids, burst in on her with their hugs and kisses and congratulations and giggles.

Marissa was astonished to run into Trevor and Brandon. They had been counselors with Sin, but she had had little contact with them, and they had vanished from her memory. And yet here they were, like Sin, in street clothes. She recalled them in bathing trunks and untied sneakers, knew their muscles and legs and tans, knew that Brandon wore a gold chain and Trevor had a long white scar from an old abdominal surgery. Today each wore cords, a good shirt, a fine pullover sweater—and wonder of wonders—polished leather shoes. "Wow," said Marissa in greeting. "Real shoes? With a shine? I'm all excited."

She was not excited in the least, merely surprised that Trevor and Brandon were alive, that their lives had continued to go on, when she had excused them from existence.

"Marissa!" shouted Trevor, hugging her. "Great to see you again! You look wonderful!"

Brandon kissed her as well as hugged her. "How've you been?" he demanded, as if he had been nervous since August, wondering whether she was okay.

Kissing the strangers. Awkward with the loved one.

Was this perhaps what a reunion consisted of?

Facile affection with people you hardly remembered, and dread over meeting your friends?

Trevor and Brandon shook hands with Sin, and the boys walloped each other on the back, and laughed, and ran out of things to say.

Marissa wondered if Cathy had gone out with Trevor or Brandon ever again. Cathy had had them on each side of her, the way you might have horses for an old-fashioned carriage: the dark one offset by the light one, matched in weight and stride.

"So who else is coming?" said Sin, as if sixty seconds had used up his attention span for Trevor and Brandon, and now he was ready for the interesting people.

"Cathy is," said Trevor. "I checked the RSVP list on the Mayflower Room wall. Wait'll you see that meeting room. Charles has got photographs of the camp in winter, and they're creepy. It's not like anything you remember."

Marissa's heart sank, and not over the condition of Camp Men in winter. What would gray and cream and crimson be against the silver and gold cruelty of Cathy Coatsworth?

"Heath coming?" Brandon asked her.

He'll be Heath forever, now, Marissa thought. His Camp nickname—Dark—is gone. It made him soft and remote, to be called Dark. But he's Heath now, and his real personality is harsh and desperate. "I don't know," she told Brandon.

"God, I hope so," said Brandon. "I've really been following that case. I even started reading the *Wall Street Journal* every day because it's got the most detailed coverage."

"But not the goriest," said Trevor, listing the papers he liked to read to get the really juicy details on the family.

"They had to sell their Lake Placid summer place to pay lawyers' fees."

"Get out of town. They have millions stashed away. They don't have to sell a single silver spoon."

"Sure they do. That way they can pretend to be broke and pitiful, but when the whole thing cools off, they'll go to Luxembourg or something and live on what they've got in banks in Europe."

Was this what Heath had to listen to each day? Marissa wondered. An analysis of the family tricks?

"I'll tell you guys a few details that will make your hair stand on end," said Sin.

"No!" cried Marissa. "Sin—you—you can't!"

Brandon and Trevor said if Sin had a scoop he should sell it. Somebody besides Heath Hesper senior should make a buck out of this; newspapers were willing to pay for those details and Sin could make a classical buck.

Marissa took Sin's hand and held it tightly, as if she could press out of his skin any desire to make money off her gossip. "Sin, let's go up to Reception. I have to get my room key. And I have to set my bag down somewhere." She hauled him off with her. "Sin," she whispered, "you just can't tell them the things I told you. They're secrets."

"No, they're not. You told me."

"But—but, Sin, Heath trusted me not to."

some creature in polyester pants to finish getting her stuff out of another machine, so Lynn could do the jeans and darks in it.

Lynn hated laundry. She hated laundromats and all people who used them. She hated Saturdays.

She and her mother sat on orange plastic seats to watch their laundry swirl behind glass doors. "I hate laundry," said Lynn's mother. "I hate laundromats. I hate Saturdays."

They giggled. Lynn kept thinking of Claudia's Saturday.

"It's so neat being divorced," said Lynn. "You get all these new relatives. Now, Claudia has this terrific aunt, Wendy, or Gertrude, or something, who keeps ponies in Boston."

"I would rather have an Aunt Gertrude who did the laundry for me," said her mother.

Lynn said her family was really quite dull and she never got to have any new relatives. Her mother said maybe Lynn would get lucky, and marry into a family full of people who kept ponies in Boston.

The clothes finished washing. They jammed the wet things into baskets and hauled them back to the car. "Our dryer had better work," said Lynn darkly. "I sure don't want to come back here today."

She looked at her mother for reassurance.

"Do you know that Claudia doesn't do a single household chore?" said Lynn. "Not at her father's house and not at her mother's."

Lynn's mother said nothing.

"And how come I don't get to go alone to big

cities? If you can trust me to do the laundry," Lynn said, "how come you can't trust me to go up to Boston when I feel like it?"

"That is the most ridiculous thing I ever heard. You're twelve. You can't go hundreds of miles to some—I mean—there's crime—or you could get lost—or—I don't know, terrible things could happen."

Lynn made a face. Just once in her life, she would like something terrible to happen. They reached home, each lugging a heavy basket of wet clothes inside.

"You don't mean Claudia went alone to Boston, do you?" said Lynn's mother. "How could she? Didn't her aunt Gertrude or her mother or somebody drive her?"

"Course not. She took the train. By herself. She had her suitcase ready, and we walked to the train station, and she got on the train for Boston."

Lynn's mother stared at her. The stare made Lynn uneasy. She squirmed. "Well, she did, Mother!"

"But, Lynn—the train to Boston doesn't stop here. We're a local station."

8

————

Claudia was at the top of the silver stairs!

Violet forgot Jamie and Marissa and her pink ski jacket and began laughing. She wanted to cry out in celebration! Claudia had come!

Vi was flooded by memories.

Camp—O Camp!

How many nights she and Claudia had sat up together, while the other girls slept. They would eat Twinkies that Vi's mother mailed in and tell each other sad stories. Vi's sad stories were all made-up and Claudia's were all true. Outside, the forest would rasp and creak, the loons on the lake would utter death calls, and Big Foot would trample dry branches. But inside, they were cozy: Claudia sitting up in her sleeping bag like a large navy-blue worm, and Vi wrapped in her blankets like a pink designer caterpillar.

Vi darted up the silver steps, remembering the

cliff walk and how they used to slide down it on their fannies, so you could tell a Violet girl by the condition of her jeans. How Claudia had grown in three short months! From a girl as thin as a bookmark to the first curves of a teenager. Vi couldn't wait to—

And Cathy strolled across the silver balcony.

Violet would have known Cathy anywhere. That gold hair, too gold to be real, cascading over the slim shoulders, gleaming like precious metal against the well-chosen, simple, dark wool of Cathy's sophisticated dress. Cathy stood in the midst of the glittering chandeliers and outshone everything there.

Vi's foot stayed where it was.

Her boots seemed too large, her dress too old for her, her colors wrong. Vi would have to walk up toward Cathy, as if toward a golden goddess, and when she arrived, Cathy would be tall and beautiful and Vi would be short and dowdy.

There was nothing worse than being the right person inside the wrong clothes. You could not show off your personality when your clothes got in the way. Vi didn't care what anybody said; in the wrong clothes, you were the wrong person.

Vi swallowed, took another step, and steeled herself. Cathy, with her splendidly vicious timing, would want details on Jamie. This is it, thought Vi. The most hateful, petty, mean person at Camp Men, will now set me up as her victim-of-the-reunion.

And then Claudia—*her* Claudia—kissed Cathy hello.

How great was the power of a hug!

For the entire two seconds of its duration, Cathy was once more whole, the self-hatred erased.

"Why, Claudia," she said, almost weeping with gladness, "how are you? I'm so glad to see you."

But Claudia pulled herself away as if Cathy had been a telephone pole to chain a bike to, and said, "There's Roxanne. And Dana!" Claudia bolted across the balcony to attack a couple of girls who did not look even vaguely familiar to Cathy.

She was afraid to follow Claudia. The girls were in a huddle, like a human tepee. Cathy felt excluded just watching it. If she went over there and they ignored her, she would lose even the two seconds' joy that the unexpected hug had provided. She could not imagine what had made Claudia hug her, but the aftershock still comforted her, and she clung to it as a child to a teddy bear.

Two seconds is a start, Cathy told herself. If I double it each time, next I'll feel good for four seconds. Heck, before you know it, I'll have experienced a quarter of a minute of happiness.

She turned away, trying to retain the warmth of a hug against the sterile glitter of the huge room, and looked down at the only color—the vermilion carpet two stories below.

There stood Channing's best friend.

Channing had always called him Pink, because his cheeks were oddly red, as if he had poorly applied a lot of rouge. He was very slim, almost weedy, but wore wonderful clothes, and blew his hair dry so that it haloed around his head and fell lightly over the tops of his horn-rimmed glasses. Pink always looked studious and rich, as if he went to Yale, or was the younger brother of an English lord.

The police had asked her if she knew any of Channing's partners, but she'd said no, of course not, and Channing had agreed that of course Cathy didn't know anybody.

For all his chatter to the police, Channing had, in the end, given remarkably little information. He'd claimed to be both mastermind and errand boy, all territory his, all work his. The police were skeptical; it had been too big an operation for one person.

I know Pink, thought Cathy now.

Channing wasn't protecting me from the police, she thought. He was protecting Pink.

She did not know Pink's real name, nor his address, nor where he went to school. Why had she never wondered about it? It was just more proof of her boundless conceit.

Pink turned a bit, and peered past a woman in an evening gown, searching for somebody or something. Then he walked a few paces to the left, took a pipe out of his pocket, and began tamping away at it. Cathy was quite sure that Pink did not smoke a pipe. It was a display to kill time.

Or a signal.

Suddenly she thought—*next he'll look up*. He'll see me. No, no, no, no! I came here for a fresh start, not to renew an old ugly criminal acquaintance!

Cathy stumbled along the balcony, trying to stay invisibly in the middle of it. The fire stairs were closer than the elevators, and she scurried up them, feeling rodentlike in her crouched rush.

The hotel stairs were spooky. They had been vacuumed, and dusted, but Cathy felt as if she were the only person to have used them in years. She was suddenly in a vacant building, in another time zone. The carpet muffled her footsteps and the stairwell rose up and up, like in a nightmare. Red was the color of the wallpaper and carpet, and Cathy blended into it, and she ceased to be a person and was just part of the hotel.

She ran out of breath, her leg muscles trembled, and the door to the fifth floor, when she reached it, was very heavy. Fire regulations? she wondered dimly, pushing her entire weight against the door.

It opened two inches silently, unwillingly, as if only *some* people were allowed on the fifth floor and not necessarily Cathy.

A tiny figure in sweatpants, so far down the long long hall she seemed telescoped, was running toward her crying, "Marissa! Marissa!"

She started to say, "No, it's Cathy," when she saw Marissa, standing with her back to Cathy about four rooms away. Even from behind, there was no mistaking Marissa. That thick mane of dark hair, so unexpectedly romantic and soft on Marissa's strong lean body. Marissa always presented a contradiction of soft and strong, so that people wanted to get to know her better and find out which she really was.

"I'm so excited!" Marissa shouted to Alicia, running to meet her. "Are you excited? Are you

ready? Is everything falling into place just perfectly?"

I'm crazy or they are, thought Cathy.

She had forgotten Marissa's excesses of enthusiasm. Even the way Alicia and Marissa hugged
seemed too much for the occasion, as if they had
something else in mind altogether, while Cathy
was just attending a camp reunion. The two girls
half talked and half just made sounds. Crooning,
purring, happy sounds. Reunion murmurs?
thought Cathy. There was something so touch-
ing—so animal about it. They were exploring each
other with touch and look.

Perhaps a reunion was a very basic human need,
like meals or clean hands. To see another person
once more, whom you once loved, required certain
cries and postures.

"Gosh! What great clothes!" said Alicia admir-
ingly. Cathy quite agreed. Marissa was perfectly
dressed—sophisticated colors and cut, but with
her hair left loose and deeply waved.

"Charles made me wear my Camp Men stuff,"
said Alicia, "but you stay in that, Marissa. Don't
even think about getting into a Camp Men T-shirt.
Somebody has to look decent at this reunion. Now
I have to fly. I just want to warn you about one of
your roommates."

Cathy sucked in her breath. No, no, no, no!
Don't warn her against me! Give me a chance!
Please.

"My cousin Brie," said Alicia. "You know how
families are. She's one of the party, I couldn't help

it. You be nice to her the way you always are, okay? Great. 'Bye now."

Cathy sagged so heavily with relief her weight pushed the door open the rest of the way and they turned and saw her. Cathy felt as if her whole life were at stake. "Hi, Marissa. Hi, Alicia."

Marissa stared at her. Woodenly she said, "Hello, Cathy. How have you been?"

"Fine, thank you. I guess—we'll be sharing a room, then."

"You're the one the hotel gave the fourth bed to," said Alicia in an accusing voice.

Cathy wet her lips. If they made noises now, she thought, it would be growls. Maybe a hiss or two.

"Well, as I say, I have to fly. I'll see you both in the Mayflower Room." Alicia walked in the opposite direction, toward the elevators.

Cathy's hands were shaking. For something to do, she attempted to open the door of their room, but she could not get the key in the lock. The key was actually a plastic computer card, and she could not seem to locate the slot it went into. The seconds ticked by. The door remained shut. Cathy felt as if she would stay hunched over the stubborn door while Marissa looked silently on for years.

"I'll do it," said Marissa. Swiftly and efficiently she let them into the room, turned on the lights, and went to the window to check out the view.

It was an enormous room. Huge windows looked out over treetops bare and black against the gray sky, like fork prongs in the clouds. Long brocade curtains in deep forest green framed the window, and the carpet and bedspreads were the same color, with gold fleur-de-lis patterns, giving the room a heavy, queenly French feel, dragging at your heels for a procession. On one side, a double bed was flanked by French provincial white-and-gold chests of drawers. Opposite the double bed were two single beds, separated by similar chests. On each bed rested a small wicker basket of hotel gifts—a taste of chocolates, a drop of perfume.

How like camp it was!

Each girl looked quickly at the beds to analyze the assets and drawbacks of each position—to stake out the best bed before another camper arrived to seize it.

Marissa picked the more isolated single bed, putting her suitcase possessively on top of it.

Cathy was nearly sick with making her decision. It seemed worse than a summit meeting of the Western powers—having to decide between the other single (thus partnering herself with Marissa, who surely had other plans) or taking half the double (thus sharing not just the room but also the bed with somebody who might also be hostile to her).

Perhaps it would be Brie. Cathy set her overnight bag on the double bed, on the bathroom side, as far from Marissa as she could get and glanced up from under her eyelashes to see if this pleased Marissa.

Marissa was still looking out the window.

"How was your autumn?" Cathy said desperately. "Have you seen much of Sin or Heath?"

"A little."

Cathy hunted for another sentence. "I guess I'll fix my hair before I go down," she said.

"Fine," said Marissa. "I'll run on down now."

And Cathy was left alone in the huge room, holding her hairbrush for hair that was perfect already.

9

Vi felt as lonely as a tiny child who cannot see her mother in the Christmas-shopping crowd. Carols may play and Santa may laugh—but nobody holds your hand.

Quietly she turned on the staircase, squeezed between two other guests, and walked away. Get a grip on yourself, she thought. It was only a hug, and after all, that is the definition of a reunion, isn't it? Hugs all around?

But with Cathy? And not only had Claudia vanished as soon as she'd hugged Cathy, but Cathy had stared long and hard past Vi into the crowds below, as if acknowledging Vi's presence was too silly for Cathy to bother with.

Vi took a different route to the Mayflower Room. She had a backache. Vi was always reading about people whose hearts ached, but emotion took Vi between the shoulder blades, like a mugger's knife. I wish I could have a back rub, she thought. Maybe I'll skip the reunion. Go to the hotel masseuse instead.

Jamie had given her a back rub once. She had curled like a cat beneath his strong fingers.

The lump in Vi's throat hardened into an impenetrable cancerous mass. She wouldn't be able to say hello to anybody at the reunion because she would have choked to death.

The Mayflower Room was a hundred times larger than the Mayflower herself had been. Murals of Pilgrims and Cape Cod, cranberry bogs, and Indians planting corn sprawled around the room. The huge chandeliers here, in an attempt to look Puritan, had tiny black shades instead of sparkling prisms of crystal.

The windows faced the water. In late November, few boats were in Long Island Sound. The sea was gray and gloomy, and the wind shredded it into sharp waves and slapped them against the rocks where, in summer, yachts docked.

The room was far too large for the number of people there. It was not cozy. Vi was among the first arrivals, and the few returning campers so far were lost in the vastness of the place. Too bad we really aren't on a tiny ship, thought Vi. Then we'd have to talk to each other; we'd be crammed in rib to rib.

She surveyed the crowd, hoping for a good selection of handsome teenage boys.

So far, there were two knots of kids about nine or ten looking sorry they had come. A few old men who had probably been counselors when Charles's father owned the camp were alone in the middle of the room, pretending to laugh, and three women in their thirties blocked a window.

Smart people knew better than to arrive on time. Nobody with intelligence would show up first. You wanted to slip into a crowd, not stand all alone like an unwanted cheerleader at a nonexistent game.

Vi could not think of where to stand. She could turn her back on the room, stand by the enormous fire in the stone fireplace, pretending to be chilled. She could also pretend to be hungry and wander past the refreshments. Or, of course, she could make friends with a few women twice her age.

Charles yelled, "Vi! Come on over here and meet Mr. Delamere. He was a camper fifty-three years ago, can you believe that?"

Easily, thought Vi, surveying the wrinkles on Mr. Delamere. I'm only surprised it wasn't a hundred years ago. Somehow he was confusing. She had expected recent campers here; people with vivid memories. How could somebody even remember that camp existed when they'd experienced it all that long ago? Or care?

Mr. Delamere began telling her how camp had been in his day. "All boys back then," he informed her. "Girls and suchlike came later."

Vi felt even gloomier. Had nothing changed in fifty-three years? Would girls and suchlike always come later?

"Name tags!" trumpeted Charles. Vi was embarrassed for him, in his red shorts, showing hairy legs that had lost their tan. Charles wrote out her tag for her, in huge letters, a piece of tape that stretched across her entire chest. V I O L E T!! He wrote as if she were shouting out her own name.

Vi turned her back on him to peel the name tag off as quickly as possible.

"Vi, Vi, Vi, Vi, Vi!" screamed Alicia.

Oh, the sound of one's own name in a lonely room!

Vi swung about, hurled herself on Alicia, and they talked at the same time.

"I'm so glad a real person showed up."

"I didn't know what on earth I was going to say all afternoon," agreed Alicia.

"I love your gown, it's so romantic. Did you go into New York for it?" teased Vi.

Alicia stroked her jeans and sweatshirt. "Specially designed for me," she admitted cheerfully. "Actually, Charles would probably love it if I wore this to the wedding. Would you believe he wanted the wedding in Maine? In November? At the camp? By the dock?"

They shuddered simultaneously. Vi tried to imagine the limousines and flowers, minister and bridesmaids, musicians and guests on that rutted road in the icy November winds, the trees stripped bare of leaves, the mountain gaunt. The little cabins shuttered tight and their doors boarded up. All the nets gone from the playing fields, and the boats locked in their shed. With, no doubt, the tenth snow of the season beginning just as the bride arrived.

The vision was so sad that Vi hurt for Charles.

Weddings—which were life and love, gaiety and

joy forevermore—in a place where joy was planned as a two-week session?

A two week session of love. It was a horrifying thought. Her mother would like it; it would fit right into her theory that there was no reason for weddings as they simply led to divorce, anyway.

"Vi, darling, cheer up. We're going to have a great time this afternoon. Now where is Jamie? I expected to see you coming in on his muscular arm. I want to hear all the details. Who wins the bets? Claudia or Janey? I believe they told you to keep score of the major dates, minor dates, and important kisses."

Vi had to laugh. It all seemed so silly. "Don't ask, Alicia, because Jamie never called me. Not once. It was definitely a summer romance."

Alicia was shocked. "I really thought it was more than that, Vi! Jamie was so attentive! He seemed to adore you. He even let that wasp sting him he was staring after you so hard during field day."

Vi shrugged. She was afraid of crying.

But Alicia could not get off the topic. She was rallying already, making plans for how to bring them back together through a reunion game. She seemed to think this would be very romantic, especially since it was also her wedding day. "Think about your own romance," Vi advised her.

"No, no," said Alicia. "Jamie RSVP'd. He's coming. So we must capitalize on this situation."

Vi hated it when people made you sound like the stock market. She was rescued by, of all people, Trevor, Brandon, and Sin. Trevor hugged her. Brandon bent down to kiss her. Sin picked her up by the waist and held her at eye level before kissing her. It was pretty wonderful, to be fluffy and blond and five foot one and at your camp reunion.

"So how are you?" she said to Trevor.

He said he was fine.

Brandon admitted to being fine also.

Even Sin said he was fine.

"And how are you?" they asked.

Violet was fine.

Nobody had anything else to say. They stood looking away from each other, as if they had started a camp game: how to have four people in a circle and not focus your eyes on any of them. Vi managed a laugh. Sin joined in. Trevor and Brandon chuckled.

Vi thought, I don't care about these people. Where's Jamie? Where's Marissa? Where are the people who count? Is this any way to spend Thanksgiving weekend?

Claudia's mother and Jonathan felt that Thanksgiving itself was a wonderful and satisfying tradition, but that the rest of the weekend left something to be desired. They hoped to start a tradition of giving a really spectacular party on the Saturday and had invited seventy-five people. Of course, some were to be away for the entire weekend, but most were delighted to have something scheduled for Saturday. Claudia's mother was determined to prove that she and her second husband gave even better parties than she and her first husband used to.

The house was frantic.

Jonathan was making the hors d'oeuvres, and the kitchen was a mess, although it smelled wonderful.

"What about Claudia's room?" she said. "It's disgusting in there. She hasn't picked up in about a year, and the junk is knee deep." This was not an exaggeration. Claudia did not have high standards.

"Just keep the door shut so nobody sees it," advised Jonathan. "Oh, I have to bring up the wine, almost forgot." He ran down to the cellar.

Claudia's mother switched on the vacuum cleaner to give the hall carpet another pass. She had had the house entirely redone after the divorce. While the old decor had been deep, intense navy blue, and hot dark gold, the new decor was creamy and soft and gentle. Most of the guests had not yet seen it, and she could hardly wait to hear their compliments.

The vacuum cleaner roared. Claudia's mother thought of the party. Jonathan chose wines. Neither of them heard the telephone.

Lynn's mother gave up after twelve rings.

Cathy's right hand had started shaking when she first saw Marissa, and it was still shaking long after Marissa had walked out of the room. It shook when Cathy held the hairbrush, and it shook when she rested the brush in her lap. Perhaps her hand represented her entire life and outlook. Shaky.

Marissa might just be in a bad mood. Or have a headache. Or Sin is waiting for her in the lobby. But probably, Marissa remembered all too clearly the summer months when Cathy had been mean and hateful.

I can't go to this reunion, thought Cathy. Did I seriously believe Marissa and Vi and Alicia would have forgotten anything and be ready to embrace me?

Cathy smoothed the green bedspread so no wrinkles showed to give a clue that she had ever been there. She walked out of the room, took the elevator downstairs, avoided the crush of incoming campers in the front lobby, and walked toward the back exit.

Trying to converse with Heather Anne's dear old friends was very heavy going. Nobody could think of anything to say. Finally Heather Anne suggested a nice ride in the countryside. Everybody leaped gratefully at this idea, and they all piled into the car. In November, after rain and before snow, no countryside is very pretty, but they pretended it was.

Lynn's mother called that house, too, to ask about the odd arrangement for Boston travel, but nobody answered the phone.

Cathy went out the back exit, where taxis were gathered. This exit, too, was glamorous and wide, but it had none of the vastness of the front lobby and none of the silver of the central light shaft. She was amazed to see a clutter of reporters, their cameras at the ready, their microphones up, all spread about the steps, yelling at some man getting out of a taxi. The reporters literally pinned the man to the taxi, shouting questions at him. There was a sick glee in their voices, as of hunters cornering a young fox. The air throbbed with their pleasure.

"You leave the house in order to make some kind of deal, Mr. Hesper?" shouted one reporter.

"What happened to the Ferrari collection, Mr. Hesper?"

"What's the real story about the Lake Placid property?"

"Who are you meeting here, Mr. Hesper? All dressed up for some special occasion? Is this another financial arrangement you're pulling off for your father?"

"What's that you're hiding under your coat, Mr. Hesper?"

It was Heath!

When she'd been at camp, Channing had written Cathy about the Hesper family scandals. She had been the first to identify "Dark" as Heath Hesper junior, and she had gone out of her way to taunt him more than once. Marissa knew, and Vi knew, and they hated her for that, too. Now she saw him, face set, eyes trying to look through the uplifted arms of the reporters to find a safe place, a passage into the hotel. He was as handsome as ever, but that oddly twisted smile he had—the campers used to say he'd had a stroke, as only half his face smiled at a time—had grown into a twisted frown now. He looked like a statue for unhappiness.

He looks, thought Cathy, the way I feel. She had not thought of Heath once during her own scandal. Typical, she said to herself. You are on the fringe, nearly untouched if you get right down to it, by your own bad judgment, and here is a guy whose father is destroying the whole family, a guy whose face has been changed in only three months by what he's been through—and you never even thought of him. Only of yourself.

Heath was wearing a handsome, black dinner jacket with satin lapels. He was clutching it together at the front as if his life depended on it. The reporters wanted to know what he was hiding beneath his jacket. Money? Maps to treasure? They laughed viciously.

But Cathy saw a tiny flash of yellow and red, and she thought—*it's the camp logo.* For a joke, he's wearing his Camp Men T-shirt with his dinner jacket. He can't let them know about the camp reunion or they'd come and spoil it for everybody. They must follow every member of Heath's family door-to-door. Oh, poor, poor Heath!

Heath tried to get back in the taxi, but the driver grinned. "I'm off duty now, kid."

The reporters laughed.

In a high clear voice, the sexiest one she possessed, Cathy said, "Gentlemen, kindly let me through. Mr. Hesper and I have a dinner date and you are making it quite impossible for us to reach the restaurant."

It was a very odd hour for a dinner date, but it was all she could think of on short notice. She tossed her hair. Her looks were elegant, even breathtaking; the wool of her deep crimson sheath was rich; and the gold of her hair, finer than jewels.

She extended a hand toward Heath, and the strangest expression came over his face. He was trying not to laugh. Good, thought Cathy. Probably the first time in weeks. I know the feeling.

The reporters began taking pictures of Cathy, which she enjoyed, and she postured for them, and gave them secret smiles. When somebody yelled, "Hey, honey, you getting any of that Hesper money?" she said, "My dear, I definitely have enough of my own."

The reporters followed them into the hotel. Cathy sashayed on, thinking—where do I take him from here? How do we escape?

Walking toward her was Pink.

So that's what it means to be trapped! thought Cathy, her heart missing beats, her knees turning to jelly. A photograph of me with Heath is one thing—but me with Pink? Never, never, never!

She jerked Heath's hand, and they dashed to the elevators, leaping into one just as the doors closed. They got out at the first stop, raced to the stairs, and ran on up to the fifth floor. Cathy got her key card into the slot on the first try, yanked open the door, and they jumped in, slamming it behind them.

"That was pretty neat," remarked Heath. "Just like a TV chase. A person would think you'd done this before."

Cathy burst into tears.

Heath looked as if he would have preferred a dozen hostile reporters any day. "I can't stand it," he said. "Don't do that, Cathy, please. Cathy don't cry. Come on, stop. Please?"

She did not stop.

She wasn't just crying, she was bawling.

Heath kissed her.

Another boy might have handed her a Kleenex, but Heath kissed her. It worked brilliantly. "I'm sorry," said Cathy, finding a Kleenex on her own. "It's just that so few people have had any use for me lately."

They sat on the double bed. The hotel gift basket tumbled into Heath's lap. "Smelling salts maybe?" he suggested, holding up a small bottle.

"No. That's toilet water."

"I've always thought that was a disgusting name for perfume," said Heath.

Cathy undid the stopper of the toilet water and sniffed it. It was very nice. She said, "Oh, Heath, I know you have enough troubles of your own, but can you stand to listen to mine?"

10

Sin Franklin seemed confused by the reunion, as if he had expected a different crowd entirely. The room filled. Every few minutes a little boy raced up to Sin to talk about how Sin had taught sailing and waterskiing. Kids popped up like empty bottles on a production line. Memories were poured in. Then they rolled down the conveyor belt for the next former counselor to cap them off.

All summer Vi had admired Sin. Thick blond hair like white sea foam against the golden wave of his tan, nose slathered in zinc, a whistle hanging on a lanyard around his neck. (The lanyard might be purple and white, or brown and blue, or pink and yellow; it was always the gift of a camper, handmade in arts and crafts, of narrow plastic ribbon you found only in camp, used only in camp, and for that matter, *liked* only in camp.)

And all summer Vi had restricted herself from

falling in love with Sin because Marissa worshipped him and, therefore, had a prior clearance, so to speak. Once Jamie had started seeing Vi, Vi forgot the very existence of the other boys, anyhow.

Now it seemed to Vi that Sin and the other boys didn't even *have* much existence. Nobody was saying anything worth repeating. They were babbling. Desperately making noise.

"Listen to us," said Vi. "We sound so stupid. We're trying to cover for something. What do you think it is?"

The boys were silenced.

Sin frowned and looked off toward the entrance.

Brandon took a handful of cheese sticks from a passing waiter.

Trevor shifted his feet nervously. "I think," he said unexpectedly, "it's because we're not official. When you're a counselor, you have a job and a place to stand. Little rules to follow, little people to guide, little cabins to fill. But now we're just hanging around."

Immediately for Vi, Trevor attained personality and was clearer in her vision than either Sin or Brandon, who acted as if this subject were vulgar and unwanted.

Trevor said, "I bet we'd all do better if we had on our T-shirts, like the invitation said. It would sort of tug us into camp. We aren't dressed for camp, and yet this *is* camp."

Vi loved to talk about clothing. (She had informed Charles on the opening day of camp, when he'd complained about the amount of clothing she'd brought, "But, Charles, life *is* clothing." This had not cemented her relationship with Charles.) Vi said now, "I know. I made a mistake in wearing this, anyway. My older sister really picked it out for herself." She looked down at the dark crumpled colors that swirled and blended and belonged on Jasmine. "I feel like the second act of a school play," she confided.

Trevor began laughing soundlessly, accompanied by a wide grin and shaking shoulders. "Vi, we're going to regret our analysis. Look to your left."

To her left the crowd had built considerably. Men and women who had attended camp twenty or thirty years ago. Little kids whose first two weeks away from home had been last summer. Dozens and dozens of them now filling up the formerly empty Mayflower Room.

And Charles . . . pushing a wheelbarrow.

A really truly wheelbarrow, with red wooden sides and a single fat front wheel and metal tips on the curved wooden handles. It was difficult to imagine Charles pushing this through the lobby of the Hilton, among the Gucci bags and the Samsonite luggage.

Stacked in the wheelbarrow were Camp Men T-shirts, years and years of old and new, faded and bright, extra large and children's small, like a history of Maine camp T-shirts.

"Put one on!" Charles was directing. "Doesn't matter what you're wearing. If you did not come in a T-shirt, this goes over what you've got on."

His first candidate was a plump middle-aged

woman who, the moment she tugged her extra large T-shirt over her designer sweater, looked positively obese; it gave her another twenty-five pounds. She and her companions giggled insanely, poking each other's latest, quickest weight gain. Before Vi's very eyes, they became the campers they had been many years ago, girlish and silly and happy with the latest dumb prank.

Vi studied her own layers, her belted loose shirt, her scarf and heavy rope necklaces. "Not me. If I wear a T-shirt over this, I'll look—"

"You'll look just like everybody else," said Charles firmly.

"A person goes to camp to become an individual," said Vi, trying not to accept a T-shirt.

"A person goes to camp to become an individual who can also function as part of a team," said Charles. "I never had any use for your shenanigans, Violet, and I won't take them now. Have a medium."

Vi snarled at her medium.

Trevor said, "Do you remember the time Vi and Marissa and Alicia came over to our side of the camp, Charles, and Vi thought there was a bat in her hair, and she screamed so loud all the boys came streaming out of dinner to rescue her?"

Charles groaned and moved on with his wheelbarrow, obviously shaken by memories of Violet.

"And how Vi was always telling horror stories to her girls at midnight," put in Brandon, "so we'd wake up to the sounds of murder in the girls' camp? And Charles would rush over, either rowing himself to death or driving the Jeep through the woods, and it was just the next episode of the Green-Eyed Maniac?"

Vi had been partial to stories in which a green-eyed maniac suffocated little campers by lowering the upper bunk on their faces.

"My boys always felt left out," said Trevor. "I never had any stories that good."

Vi was filled with joy. It was like laughing gas. Oh, the pleasure of being the center of attention! Vi wanted to stand there forever while they remembered her. She considered briefly telling a few stories about what *they* had done, but since she, Vi, was so much more interesting, it seemed a shame to break in.

"Games!" shouted Charles. "Time for games! We've got to get to know each other again, people! By the time this reunion is over, everybody here will be friends! Good friends! Whether they went to camp in nineteen eighty-eight or in nineteen fifty-eight!"

"Why would we want to be friends with somebody who went in fifty-eight?" asked Violet. "If I needed a friend that old, I could have brought my mother."

"Hush," said Alicia, following in Charles's tracks and trying to whip up enthusiasm. "And cooperate, Violet. You were always a thorn in Charles's side. Be charitable. The man is getting married in a few hours."

"Boy, you'd never know it," observed Vi. "He looks more like a guy who's going to hike the Appalachian Trail in a few hours."

"Don't suggest it," pleaded Alicia. "He probably would."

Alicia and Vi giggled, and Vi wanted to know what the honeymoon plans were. Vi loved to plan her own wedding. She liked planning her first apartment, too, and her first budget, and meals and furniture and job. She hoped to marry somebody without too many plans, as Vi had enough to go around and did not wish to compromise any.

"Exclusively four-star hotels in Paris, Rome, and London," said Alicia. "No tents, backpacks, or sneakers allowed."

Vi could only applaud this choice.

A big, overweight ex-camper from the fifties boomed out, "I guess camp fees are making you pretty financially successful, then, little lady, if you two can go gallivanting off to hotels in Paris all the time."

"One does not honeymoon all the time," said Alicia irritably.

"Some of us don't even date all the time," said Vi.

"You know what I remember?" said Sin, who found the topic of honeymoons entirely without merit and went back to camp memories. "That dance Cathy taught us."

Alicia and Vi rolled their eyes at each other. Camp memories of Cathy were not cherished by any of the girls.

On the other hand, they had all learned and loved the short dance Cathy had taught as a warm-up. It was a wild, rock-style body shake, to which you shouted a rhythmic cheer and twitched the appropriate muscles.

"So shake your ankles—two—three—four!" began Sin.

Immediately any camper who had been at camp the previous summer set down food and drinks anywhere and joined him in the second line.

> *"Your knees—two—three—four*
> *your hips—two—three—four."*

"I always liked the hip part best, didn't you?" Sin said.

Vi was busy getting ready to shake her tummy, but she took a moment to follow Sin's eyes. Just whose hips had he liked best?

In the entrance, framed by two, green plastic trees, stood Marissa.

I'm going to cry first, thought Vi. Then I'll run up to her, showering tears left and right.

She wanted to holler, the way they had in the dining hall at Camp Men. *You guys are late to dinner!! What did you do in that shower anyway—try to drown a seven-forty-seven?*

But Marissa looked the way Jasmine had tried to make Vi look. Elegant and older, calmer, and hardly even familiar. This was the girl who had arranged Ping-Pong relays in the water? Who had been the best horse in the pretend rodeo?

Vi took two steps toward Marissa and faltered.

Then Marissa saw Vi, and came bounding past chairs, campers, Pilgrims, even Sin, shouting, "Vi! Vi! Vi!"

The boys were forgotten.

The reunion was forgotten.

The Hilton, the waiters, the strangers, and the friends.

All were forgotten. Nobody existed for Marissa and Vi except each other.

Mercifully they were not aware that half the packed room had fallen silent to stare, filled with sadness and envy. For here was the reunion they had all come there to experience. A voice shouting across the room, calling out *your* name. Eyes misting with tears, hugs that would not stop but went on and on, as if squeezing friendship back into shape.

By now there were some two-hundred-fifty guests, the youngest eight; the oldest, seventy-nine. And all who could see Marissa and Vi paused and yearned. Nobody could hear what the girls said to each other, but they made up the dialogue in their minds.

How are you?

I'm fine, how are you?

Why didn't you write?

Because I'm such a dope.

It doesn't matter. I'm so glad to see you.

And I'm so glad you're here.

People had to turn away, for the real reunion they were seeing made their own seem empty.

Charles, however, did not deal in heavy-duty emotion. "Violet, you have not put your T-shirt on," he said angrily. "Hello, Marissa, good to see you. Put on a T-shirt, please. Think you can escape the rules as usual, Violet?"

Vi threw her arms around Charles, flinging her reunion love even his way. "Oh, no, Charles! I love rules. I absotively possilutely thrive on rules. Give me a T-shirt. Give me ten T-shirts. I'll wear one as a neckpiece and tie back my hair with another, and—"

"Vi, must you always do everything to excess?"

"Yes," said Vi firmly.

She and Marissa joined the boys, and the group of them laughed continually, staring at each other and at the other campers in their ridiculous T-shirts. Children in jeans and sweatshirts were bottled up in T-shirts two sizes too small. Counselors out of college who had come back to show off their success in the world (designer dresses and fine three-piece suits) now wore white T-shirts with suit and dress sleeves poking out and scarves and ties making peculiar chest lumps.

And then it all fell apart.

Cathy, slender and willowy, scarlet and gold, appeared in the entrance. She seemed strangely medieval, a portrait painted for a cathedral—her hair a precious metal.

And who appeared beside her, but Heath—dark and handsome in a black dinner jacket, black cummerbund, black shoes—and a Camp Men T-shirt peeking between the satin lapels of his jacket.

Marissa's joy at seeing Vi evaporated. She felt fat and ridiculous, the T-shirt twisted over her sweater, and her scarf bunched up beneath as if she had extra breasts. How could Heath be here with Cathy? He had lied to her! Pretending there was nobody else to talk to, and all along he'd been talking to Cathy. Probably dating her, too.

"Ghost rocks! Ghost rocks!" cried Charles,

climbing up on top of a table. "We're going to paint rocks, just as we always do every year on the last day of camp. Everybody will write a word or paint a symbol or initials that stand for his or her feelings toward Camp Menunkechogue and all the lovely, sunny, satisfying summers gone by."

The teenagers listened to this and ignored it. They weren't going to be caught painting pebbles at the Hilton. "I," said Violet, "am overcome by emotions. Hatred of Cathy. Pity for Alicia, marrying an idiot. Joy at seeing Marissa. Total humiliation at being caught in a T-shirt when Cathy looks like God."

Trevor said, "I don't think she looks like God. God would be more muscular. I think she looks like a Russian princess."

Marissa and Vi did not care for this comparison. "Why Russian?" said Marissa darkly.

"Because standing next to Heath, she's all mysterious like him, and different, like people whose era is ending. Who are going to be shot at dawn by the revolutionaries."

Vi giggled. "I like the part about them getting shot at dawn, Trevor."

Charles was lining people up, getting them ready to paint their rocks. He even had another wheelbarrow, full of rocks (real Maine rocks, no doubt, as opposed to substitute, measly old local rocks), and paint in primary colors waited in paper cups all down the length of long, paper-covered tables.

"I bet the Hilton management didn't know about these plans for painting when Charles rented the Mayflower Room," said Sin.

"I bet they don't know about it right now," said Vi. "I bet if we find the right manager quick enough, we can stop the whole humiliating thing in its tracks."

The campers Charles's age sighed and advanced very reluctantly to the tables, as if they would rather be dead. The small children vanished to safety zones, such as under other tables. Alicia, bustling around trying to work up enthusiasm, overheard Vi's plan.

"Don't do that," she pleaded. "He's so happy. Give this to him for your wedding present. Throw yourselves into this as if it's really camp."

But of course, it was not camp.

Nobody had come here, as they had to Maine, in order to do arts and crafts, or puddle in paint. Nobody wanted to flick color around the room and have green rocks appear.

If Vi had ever seen a party that was going to fail this was it. Not one person in the Mayflower Room was willing to pick up a paintbrush and paint. Two hundred and fifty totally unwilling campers stood very still. Charles galloped around, convinced that all it would take was a little friendly prodding. Alicia's hands knotted with worry that the reunion would not go right and, therefore, would spoil Charles's mood for the wedding.

Mother was right, thought Vi. Perhaps all mothers are always right. It was very very dumb to have a combination camp reunion and wedding.

"All right you guys!" yelled Vi. She descended on a group of kids she had never seen before in her life. "T-shirts—on!" she shouted. "Brushes—ready! Rocks—forward! And . . . *paint!*" With great faked zest she leaped into the painting of her rock, splashing red paint with an abandon that would give the Hilton management cardiac arrest. "I can't draw a straight line," somebody said, weakly trying to escape. "You can't draw a straight line, anyway," said Vi, "because the rocks curve." "I can't think of anything to write," said another weakling. "Start with the alphabet," said Vi. "A is for Alicia. B is for boats."

She was like a collie, nipping at the campers' heels. She dashed hither and yon, collecting painters who were trying to hide by the punch bowl, holding up finished rocks with gasps of admiration, and mixing more colors for people who were sick of red, blue, and yellow.

It worked.

People thronged to paint. Laughter started up again. T-shirts were flecked with paint. Opinions were delivered on final rock colors.

I am a leader, Vi thought. I figured I was just a kook with yellow hair who liked mascara more than hiking. But Charles only *told* them what to do. I got them to *do* it.

Her hair prickled.

Down with all elementary school teachers' reports!

Fie on all principals who said Vi was average.

Curses on the heads of Girl Scout troop leaders who told Vi she would never earn a badge.

I, Violet, am a leader.

Claudia, having found Roxanne and Dana on the balcony, stuck to them. In company she was safe from all the worries of the weekend. The three girls linked arms, and Claudia showed them every inch of the Hilton, with the result that they were quite late in getting to the reunion. Right off, they spotted Janey and Esther, and now they were five, practically an army, and began a clandestine war with a bunch of boys, paying no attention to the reunion Charles was organizing all around them.

The boys hid under the soda table. They were going to yank the cloth out from under the glasses and try not to spill anything. Claudia had once tried this herself. All you got was Coke on the floor.

She wanted to be far away when that happened. Abandoning Roxanne, Dana, Janey, and Esther, Claudia hurried to the opposite end of the room, where all the grown-up campers were painting ghost rocks.

She was second in line to paint when hair like a fluffy yellow duckling caught her eye.

"VIOLET!" screamed Claudia.

"Gosh, it's good to see you, Marissa," said Heath. He hugged her, squashy T-shirt and all. Then he held her away from him for a better look, and finally hugged her a second time, even harder. Just so had Alicia and Vi hugged Marissa.

So that's what a reunion hug is, she thought. A double dose. Assure yourself the person is real, stand back to study the face, and then the real hug. "Hi, Heath."

"I know, I know. You're mad at me. I don't blame you for hanging up the telephone on me. I deserved it."

He had not come with Cathy after all. They had

simply landed at the door together. Marissa forgave him everything, instantly.

"I was lying on the floor at the time," Heath went on, "and I had my feet up on the wall, which left perfect black prints from my shoes, and I was thinking how my mom was going to go crazy when she saw those black treads, and how mad you were because I was whining all the time."

If only I had known we were *both* lying on the floor with our feet up, thought Marissa. It would have made all the difference.

"Let me guess," said Brandon with a smirk. "You decided to clean up the treads and clean up your act and maybe even reform your father."

Marissa hated Brandon. She hated him with such ferocity that, when she whirled on Brandon, Heath caught her arm. "I can take care of myself, Marissa," he said very softly.

Marissa looked into Heath's face and fell in love with him. Great, she thought. Now I adore two of them. Sin *and* Heath. I have an infinite capacity to forgive, which probably means I will always love people who need a lot of forgiving. Which means I will be miserable forever. I should be in a loony bin.

She wondered what a loony bin might be. A big green garbage dumpster? The kind big enough to drive a car in? She could see all the girls crazy with love climbing in an orderly fashion into its horrid green maw, while the boys carelessly waved goodbye and found other girls.

"Love your hair like that," Heath added.

She looked like an escapee from that loony bin,

with the dumb T-shirt, but Heath did not see her clothes. He saw the girl who talked to him on the phone all those hard Monday nights.

Okay, adored one, thought Marissa, looking into Heath's eyes. Ask me out on a date.

There were a good many people between Claudia and Vi, plus a large table. Claudia showed no mercy. Black, white, old, young, fat, or thin, she shoved everybody out of her way. She hurled herself forward, only to find the table obstructing her path. She leaped on it, swung her feet over, and dropped on top of Vi, all the while screaming, "Vi, Vi, Vi, Vi, Vi!"

Older hands reached to catch the paint cups. They missed. Red, blue, green, yellow, and purple sloshed everywhere. Including on Vi's skirt.

Vi hardly noticed. I have been greeted with more noise than anybody else, she thought. My name has been shouted aloud the most. And I just found out I am a leader. So who needs Jamie?

With as much dignity as a person lying on the floor with a thirteen-year-old and five colors of paint on top of her can have, Vi said, "Hello there, Claudia. How have you been?"

They hugged in several colors.

"I knew you would do something like this!" shouted Charles. "Does anybody else spill paint? No, it's Vi. Always Vi! You'll probably do something to ruin the wedding, too, Violet. I know you, and your hot rollers and your curling irons!"

"Now, Charles," said a forty-year-old former

camper. "Let's mop it up. They're having a re-union. Isn't that what camp is all about?"

Charles sputtered and fumed while the woman grabbed a roll of paper towels and a pan of water and got to work. "I should have taken Vi's name off the computer list," he muttered.

Vi and Claudia picked themselves up. The Hilton would not be pleased. "You two go off now and get that skirt cleaned," advised the woman. "I'll clean this up. Charles, you hush."

Vi turned to run for the nearest water faucet, but first looked into the eyes of this pleasant middle-aged volunteer. Her face showed a sort of grief. She bent to cleaning as if she had needed an accident to happen, so she could busy herself with it. Had this woman come—all these years later—hoping to be remembered by friends and cabin-mates? And nobody had, or could?

Vi wanted to weep for her, but Claudia said, "Come on, Vi, we have to hurry before the stain sets. I'm really sorry about it."

"Don't be sorry," said Vi, running along with her. "I'm not sorry. All my life this will be the standard by which I measure reunions. Does anybody leap full speed over a barrier to see me?"

Nobody was talking to Cathy. Everybody had forgotten her. Instead of a golden dove to be cooed over, Cathy was a thin, unloved stranger. Her hungry eyes watched each reunion. Like the last child at nursery school to get picked up, her eyes said, *Where's my mother? Isn't she coming? Won't anybody come for me? Doesn't anybody want me?*

In an attempt to fit in, Cathy, too, had put on a T-shirt. Nobody teased her. She had stood alone to paint her rock. Nobody asked what her letters meant. Cathy had a soda, and nobody talked with her there. Heath had forgotten her. Sin (now that there was competition) was flirting much more genuinely with Marissa. Trevor's eyes followed Vi. As for Brandon, Cathy was afraid to get near him. If Brandon picked on Heath, he would certainly pick on her.

Marissa wondered what had brought Cathy. She had not liked camp. She had laughed at it. Nor had Cathy even liked any of them.

"Nice to see old Cathy getting what she deserves, huh?" said Brandon.

But it was not nice.

It was terrible.

For what on earth is more painful than a person without friends?

11

"First of all," said Vi, "I want to know why you were hugging Cathy like that at the top of the stairs."

She's jealous! thought Claudia. How wonderful. Claudia scrubbed at the red paint on Vi's skirt. "You'd better take it off."

Vi slithered out of her skirt. Jasmine's skirt, actually, she thought. To thine own self be true. If you are a ruffles and lace person, do not wear streamlined tailoring. "So?" she said to Claudia. "I'm waiting."

"I survived all September, October, and most of November without ever thinking of Cathy," admitted Claudia. "And if I *had* thought of her, they wouldn't have been nice thoughts. But you know what, Vi?"

The red paint came out completely. Vi wrung out the skirt. The only thing worse than wearing the wrong clothes to the reunion was wearing wet, wrinkled wrong clothes. "What?" she said.

"I think it doesn't matter what you shared over the summer as long as you shared anything. Good time or bad time. If you had it together, you're part of the whole memory. Cathy was a sharp, mean piece of camp, but she was the first person I saw here, so she made me feel glad."

Vi shook her skirt vigorously to try to unwrinkle it. She's wise, thought Vi. Claudia is thirteen, and she is wise. Perhaps it's all those remarriages. She wondered what Claudia would be like in years to come. Most likely she would never see Claudia again and would never know. It was an eerie thought—futures strung out like balls of string all over the world, and you could never follow any but your own.

Vi detested heavy thoughts. She shook this one off. "The weddings, Claudia. What did you wear, and did Heather Anne improve, and did Jonathan improve, and are you at peace yet?"

"How could anybody be at peace with two new stepparents?" said Claudia reasonably. "I'm at war, Vi. War." Claudia was taken with the word the moment she said it out loud, and she repeated it very softly to herself several times. War. That was it. They had won all the battles so far, but she was on new territory now. Okay, so she had had a little trouble on housing for the night. She was still going to win the war. She was not going to call home, whimpering, begging for help or money. They would have no occasion to laugh at her. She would sail through this weekend like an adult, and

116

saunter back through their front doors exactly when she felt like it, and not a minute before.

"Vi?" said Claudia. "I brought clothes to wear for the wedding. Can I change in your room?"

"Oh, sure. No problem. Great." Vi was flapping her skirt under the hot-air hand dryer.

Claudia thought Vi would probably let her sleep in her room, too. The carpets in this place were as thick as mattresses, anyhow. Claudia would take an extra pillow and blanket and sleep on the floor. That would show her parents. She didn't even want their crummy old beds. She had friends in this world who would let her sleep on their floor. So there.

Claudia was feeling cocky.

The bathroom door was flung open, and Janey, Esther, Dana, and Roxanne filled up all the floor space, hugging Vi, flapping her skirt for her, and telling her all they had done since camp drew to a close.

"Every Friday," confided Janey, "we have to give oral reports because we're taking speech this year. And every Friday, I am the hit of the class because I do another episode of the Green-Eyed Maniac. I get an A every time."

Vi was thrilled. She would have to tell Charles that she had, after all, given her cabin a skill to take home. So it wasn't swimming. We all had our gifts and telling horror stories was surely worthwhile.

"We have to give speeches, too," said Claudia, "but we can't tell stories. We have to do research and present information in an interesting yet captivating manner."

"How horrid," sympathized Vi. "The only thing worse than presenting information is pretending it's interesting."

They emerged from the bathroom just as Charles scurried past, apparently starting another fun-activity-for-Camp-Menunkechogue-returnees. "How can Alicia let Charles run around like that?" demanded Vi. "All hairy legs and a red-billed hat, like the center of a poisonous spider?"

Claudia giggled. "He's not that bad."

"I am making a vow," said Vi. "I shall never marry a man who runs around a Hilton hotel in his shorts."

"Vows, schmows," said Claudia. "Once they make up their minds to marry, they'll marry anything. Alligators, Communists, used coffee filters—people in love don't care."

"Wonderful ghost rocks, people!" cried Charles, beaming with pride. "I am so proud of the level of artistic ability demonstrated here today."

Now Charles had a large wicker basket, probably made twenty years ago in arts and crafts by a ten-year-old on the first day of basket-weaving. Lying in its messily woven center were hundreds of tiny red notebooks with microscopic printing on them:

Camp Menunkechogue Reunion

"You may not leave the Mayflower Room until you have at least twenty autographs!" shouted Charles. "This is to help you meet your fellow Camp Menunkechogue alumni!"

Marissa turned her thumb-sized notebook over

and over in her palm. "You can't even fit your thumbprint on this page, let alone a serious autograph."

"What is a serious autograph?" Heath wanted to know.

"More than a signature. A meaningful, thoughtful personal phrase or two."

"We'll have to read a lot of meaning into an *X*," said Sin, "because that's all there's room for. Give me a meaningful *X*, Marissa."

Vi, Claudia, and the three other girls joined them, and everybody grabbed an autograph book and began exchanging *X*'s.

"But you haven't told us yet about Jamie," complained Claudia. "Are you dating every weekend? Does he call you every night? What's his excuse for not being here this afternoon? Have you gone to discotheques and McDonald's and Pizza Hut together so far?"

"He never called," said Vi, using Trevor's back for a desk and writing in print so small he would never be able to read it and thus she could not be embarrassed by it: *Actually it's you I love most, Trevor, ask me out please.* "I guess Jamie was just a creep after all," she added cheerfully. She wrote *Vi* with many flourishes all over her tiny sentence, to obliterate any possibility that Trevor could ever decipher it. It was nice to know that Jamie really was the creep, after all those weepy nights of figuring *she* must be the creep or he'd have called.

"So," said Brandon suddenly, and Vi was aware of his voice being loaded, like a shotgun, "what are the room arrangements? Who sleeps with whom?"

119

The way he said it made them all uncomfortable. Their accommodations no longer seemed like a more elegant rerun of camp—the boys' side of the hall instead of the boys' side of the lake—but a sleazy picture of people sneaking around in the dark.

"Four of us are in room five-twelve," said Marissa. "Vi and me and Cathy and a cousin of Alicia's named Brie."

"Brie?" repeated Claudia, giggling. "That's a cheese. Heather Anne is always serving Brie. It's mushy and disgusting, with leathery skin. Yuck. What kind of people would call their daughter after a cheese?"

"I can't help that," said Marissa. "It's the girl's name and she's our fourth."

Cathy edged up to the group.

"I know what you mean," Vi said to Claudia, ignoring Cathy. "I thought it was bad being named for a flower. But that's piffle compared to being named for a cheese."

They exchanged autograph books, X-ing pages all around. Heath stood with his hands jammed in his pockets. His jacket was flung back and the Camp logo rose and fell as he breathed. Marissa could not look at him and could not look away from him. She was almost twitching from the exhaustion of being so near him. "Marissa?" he said suddenly, softly. "Listen. All fall I've wanted you and me to get together, but I've been wiped out by what's happening to my family. I didn't have any energy for dating or anything. I'm sort of

120

moving into another stage now, if you know what I mean."

Marissa certainly hoped she knew what he meant. They stared at each other, and the stare was so intense she had to break it off, doing so with a toss of her thick hair. She stared at the floor and then quickly back up at Heath. He started to say something more—but Sin spoke first.

"I've X'ed your book, Marissa. And it's a very meaningful, profound X. You're going to love it." He handed her the book, and hung on to her hand when she accepted it.

Somebody take a photograph, thought Marissa. I have a boy whispering in each ear.

But Sin had ended whatever Heath might have said. They were back to tiny red autograph books, and exchanging pens and pencils. Claudia and Brandon and Trevor and Vi and Janey . . .

"Thirteen to go," remarked Cathy. "That's not a very good omen." She held out her own book rather desperately, for somebody else to seize and sign.

Marissa remembered a horrible story from high school a few years ago. A graduating senior had told her, "Nobody signed my yearbook. The day of signing, they were all busy signing each other's, and nobody remembered me. My book is blank." If Marissa had a blank yearbook, she would burn it. She wouldn't keep it to remind her she had no friends.

"That's true, Cathy," said Brandon, not taking her autograph book. "You haven't had very many good omens in your life lately, have you?"

121

There was something vicious in his voice that silenced them all—made them look back and forth between Cathy and Brandon.

"You know what, Cathy?" said Brandon. "I think everybody here just reads the front page of the newspapers. They figure the only scandal worth reading about is old Heath's dad ripping off old ladies' pension funds. But they haven't read the really interesting parts of the paper, have they, Cathy?"

Cathy was very still. Her fingers were knotted around a glass of Coke. She didn't look to anybody else to rescue her. Perhaps she knew they wouldn't.

Brandon said, "Why don't you tell them about your own juicy little criminal scandals, Cathy?"

Vi snatched Cathy's autograph book and began signing it. "Brandon, you make me sick. Whatever it is, stop it." She passed the book on to Marissa. "This is our reunion. Let's just remember the good things."

"And what good things can you remember about Cathy from last summer?" said Brandon.

Vi glared at him.

Cathy shivered, alone.

And Marissa thought of the good things from camp. Buddies. You always had to have a buddy, whether you were swimming or hiking or straightening the cabin. Buddies aren't just for safety, thought Marissa, or to make chores go quicker.

Marissa put an arm around Cathy, drawing her into the circle with Heath and herself and Sin, and shutting Brandon out. "She's our friend, Brandon. That's what we remember."

Heather Anne and Claudia's father got back from their drive in the country. The dear old friends had proved to be very silent old friends, and conversation had long ago run out. Claudia's father went into the kitchen to mix drinks. Piled on the bar was the stack of Claudia's schoolbooks.

Normally he hated going to the house where he had lived for fifteen years with his first wife, but just now he was glad to have an excuse to get away. He drove on over, only to find that Eve and Jonathan were giving a huge party, and there was no place to park. He drove around the block. He could not quite see himself walking in on all the people who used to be his friends, too, and now were only her friends. And if he went up to the door, probably Jonathan would be off talking to somebody and Eve would be in the kitchen and the door would be opened by a stranger. He'd have to ask if his ex-wife could please come to the door.

He could bring the books in the morning instead. But that was childish. They had had a perfectly civilized divorce; they were the best of friends now; there was no reason he couldn't just walk up, laughing at their daughter's forgetful ways, and deposit the books. He double-parked, gathered the books, and strode to the front door.

It was opened by Jonathan, who was astonished to see him.

"Hi," said Claudia's father.

"Uh—hello there. Come on, uh, in. We—"

"No, no. I just brought Claudia's schoolbooks. She forgot them, and I know she has a report on the Constitutional Convention due next week."

Jonathan looked at him oddly. "Claudia's with you for the weekend."

"No, she isn't. She's with you."

12

The party was noisy and successful. People were eating and drinking and laughing and telling funny stories. The music Eve had put on the CD player was just right, and everybody had told her how much more cheerful and open the house seemed in its new, light colors.

Claudia's mother and Jonathan and Claudia's father stood in the kitchen with the door closed, staring at each other. Claudia's mother was absolutely furious. It was all a plot on Claudia's part to ruin her evening. When she caught up with Claudia she would kill her.

Claudia's father thought that he and Heather Anne should not have to put up with this sort of immature behavior and that this time he wouldn't yell at his daughter, he would thrash her within an inch of her life.

Jonathan said, a little more coolly, "She's probably still at Lynn's, where she spent last night."

They sagged with relief. A simple answer, requiring no punishments, no worry, only a phone call. "Lynn's mother will be pretty annoyed with me, abandoning my daughter on her doorstep for so long," said Claudia's mother, laughing and dialing.

Brandon said, "You're willing to forgive anything, aren't you, Marissa? But some things can't be forgiven. Cathy here is a convicted drug pusher. Her boyfriend, Channing, got his stuff in South America. Cathy's on parole because Daddy has influence. Not unlike our old friend Heath, huh?"

Drugs? thought Marissa. At my camp? Among my campers?

"You're exaggerating, Brandon," said Heath. "Cathy was not charged and not tried, let alone convicted and on parole. The police agreed that she wasn't involved at all. It was Channing's operation."

"You believe that?" said Brandon scornfully.

Marissa turned to Cathy. "Did it touch camp?" she said fiercely. "Did all those little kids there for the summer—"

"No!" cried Cathy. "No, Marissa, I promise. Because—that's why I came this afternoon. Life has been so awful. And camp was—camp was good."

Good. The word settled among them.

Heath folded his arms and stood behind their barrier. Why was camp good, he wondered. Because it was broken down into two-week sessions? Did goodness require organizing, like camp?

Camp was good to me, too, he thought. But normal life entered in. School, grades, teams, family, TV. Attending my father's trial. Is good still possible when all *that* is around?

Vi produced Kleenex for Cathy, and they all managed to laugh a little, and finish up their autograph books. The scene had given them an immense appetite. They attacked the refreshments with laughter and shouting.

Brandon left.

How mysterious, thought Marissa. Another one with a secret life I will never understand. He'd been boring, a nobody, at camp. He'd come here— for what? To be mean to Heath and to be sure we were all mean to Cathy? What is *his* story? What made him so mad?

But she would never know. Their paths would never cross again, and if they did, Marissa would avoid Brandon.

"You have enough sour cream on that potato chip to open your own delicatessen," remarked Sin. "So you're Cathy's best friend now, huh?"

Marissa flushed. "You can't be mean on a day when everything's supposed to be good."

So that's it, thought Heath. You schedule *good*. Maybe I need to schedule Marissa. Learn more about it. He helped himself to some Doritos, thinking about next weekend. Maybe Marissa could come into New York, and they could . . .

"So," said Sin, being friendly, not taunting like Brandon, "I understand your American history class is pretty grim these days. Teacher likes to talk about ethics while staring at you, Heath."

Heath froze. He had told nobody about that. Nobody but Marissa.

Sin added helpfully, "Marissa phones me after your Monday night calls. We talk about you a lot."

Claudia's mother put the phone down very gently, as if she were afraid of something. "Claudia told them she was visiting her aunt Gertrude in Boston. She took a train by herself this morning, supposedly to Boston, but it was a local. Lynn's mother tried to phone each of us, but nobody answered."

The men looked blank. "Aunt who?"

"Boston?"

"What does that mean?"

"I think it means that Claudia has run away from home," said her mother.

Charles produced a banjo. They sang "I Love to Go a-Wandering," and "O Susannah," and their own camp versions of "Clementine" and "Sipping Cider Through a Straw."

"And now," said Charles, "it is time to repeat the camp pledge." He stood reverently. Alicia had long ago left to get her hair done, and he was alone, ridiculous in his shorts and cap, bony knees and pale skin.

The kids jabbed each other with sharp elbows to keep from laughing at him.

> *I promise to be a friend*
> *to people around me and to the earth.*
> *I promise to love the world*
> *and all her glories.*

*I promise to encourage, to praise, and
to be patient.
To let the world know
I am a Camp Menunkechogue . . .*

The last word of the pledge was an unintelligible chorus of "girl" and "boy."

Cathy started crying again.

Heath tried to think of one single glorious thing in his life and couldn't. He could not look at Marissa. She had betrayed him to Sinclair Franklin.

Vi added another promise. To go on being a brilliant leader.

And the reunion was over.

The lines broke up, the hugs changed texture, becoming good-byes instead of hellos. Final photographs were snapped. Everybody hurried toward the exits, as if vacuum cleaners and maids were coming in on the other side and they didn't want to get caught.

Everybody seemed to know something Cathy didn't, as if they were operating on an urgent schedule she hadn't received a copy of. Or perhaps she was just out of energy. For weeks she had run on nerves, and the first act of kindness toward her, instead of restoring her strength had sapped her. She tottered while the others gamboled.

She yearned to get up to their shared room. The boys would go to their own room, the girls would wiggle out of these silly dumb T-shirts (although Cathy felt an affection so deep, she probably would save the T-shirt the way she saved yearbooks: with love, forever) and have girl talks. She and Vi and Marissa could be friends now.

Cathy did not even feel on trial. The sick horrid feeling that you will have only one chance was gone. Long talk, thought Cathy contentedly, and pleasant stories, and interrupting each other with better ones, and ordering pizza at midnight. "You know what?" she said suddenly. "Laury and Dana aren't here."

"I know," said Vi. "Isn't it odd? Laury and Dana were my triumphs. They really and truly did become better people from going to camp. And they didn't want to be at our reunion."

Cathy thought about this. Of course they might have had to go to the doctor, or visit their grandmothers, or do school projects. But probably not. "It's terrible to face people who had a hand in improving you," she told Vi. "But those two loved you, Vi, so I thought they'd come to say so."

Vi looked quickly to see how much sarcasm there was in Cathy, but she seemed to be entirely straight. What on earth were Cathy's camp memories? What "good" was she referring to that she had found in camp? Certainly not her own.

Of course, memory is silent.

Invisible.

Known only to you.

And mostly, you have to pull memory out. It doesn't arrive without permission. You can leave it alone, or let it surface.

She wondered what Jamie remembered. He was like Daniel Boone when he flexed his muscles. All the little boys wanted to grow up to be just like him. How, wondered Vi, could Jamie not want to spend a single Saturday afternoon with all his admirers?

"Honestly," said Marissa to Vi as they reached the lobby, and Sin and Heath went off in a different direction to their own room. "Boys."

"I know just what you mean."

"The only one I'm sure of is Brandon. *Species vomitus.*"

"So true. Write him off. But what about the others?"

"I don't know. Listen, did you read our horoscopes today by any chance?"

"No. Let's buy a paper."

"I want them both," said Marissa, and she did not mean both newspapers.

"Of course," agreed Vi. "And I have decided on Trevor. Which is interesting, because I'd forgotten he was alive. I won't tell him that, of course. It isn't terribly flattering. I think he would be excellent for the school's winter dance. That's in only two weeks. I've got to have at least two dates with him before I can ask him to take me to the winter dance, which means both dates have to be next weekend."

They bought a paper, ignored the headlines, and flipped, giggling, through the pages, stopping briefly at Ann Landers and the comics, and reading out loud their horoscopes.

"Wait, wait!" cried Claudia. All the girls her own age were leaving, and she had gotten lost in their camera-clicking and good-byes till next summer. She dashed to catch up to the older girls. She could not wait for the evening. It would be such fun! Nobody was funnier than Vi, anyhow, and Marissa would be there, and Cathy was turning out not to be so bad, and they would make jokes about old Brie being a cheese, and talk about the wedding. It would be the best slumber party that Claudia had ever been at. Better than camp even.

And my parents won't even know where I am, she gloated.

Claudia turned in her luggage ticket and got her ocean-liner-sized suitcase. But Vi wouldn't notice. Vi had brought four of these to camp. Claudia lurched into the up elevator with them, shoving her suitcase against an innocent person's ankles. Marissa was reading Sagittarius. "What's Taurus?" asked the woman with the damaged ankles. "Read me Taurus." So Marissa read her Taurus and was still reading it aloud as the girls got off on the fifth floor. Taurus never did hear the end of her horoscope.

"What are we going to do?" said Claudia's mother, beginning to cry.

"Now, now," said Jonathan. "She's got a good head on her shoulders. Let's not panic."

"Not panic? My thirteen-year-old daughter takes off for Boston, stopping to change trains in New Haven, and you don't want me to panic? What about people who prey on little girls? What about drugs, and rape, and prostitutes, and all the other horrible things?"

A guest came into the kitchen. "We're out of ice! Got any more? Shall I—" The guest broke off and looked at the trio.

"I'll get it," mumbled Claudia's mother, stumbling forward, knocking an empty dip bowl to the floor, and opening the refrigerator instead of the freezer. The guest fled the kitchen as soon as possible.

"We'll call the police," said Claudia's father. He was shaking. His baby girl. Alone. At night. Mad at the world, and her parents—what stupid, dangerous decisions might she make?

"We'll have to telephone all her friends. See if she told them anything," whispered Claudia's mother. "Oh, God, we'll have to admit to the whole world that our daughter ran away. Can you imagine what they'll say about divorced families then. I can hear the words *broken family* at every dinner table in town."

We did break her family, thought Claudia's father. And I have put Heather Anne first, and Eve has put Jonathan first. "We'll worry about her reasons for running away later," he said. "Right now, we have to do something constructive."

Cathy tagged along, too exhausted to contribute, just floating in the girl talk and feeling pretty good. She and Marissa had the same birth sign, which was nice, but she was too tired to tell Marissa the coincidence.

Just as they unlocked the room door, Brie appeared. They all had to introduce themselves. Brie had an appropriate name after all, for she was cheesy-looking—pale and bloated. Vi and Marissa and Cathy, and especially Claudia, carefully did not look at each other for fear of laughing out loud.

"I am utterly exhausted!" cried Vi, racing around the room with enough energy to win a footrace.

She opened her suitcase, hung up a dress, peeled off her T-shirt, and whipped out her hair dryer and hot rollers and makeup. "Oh, the emotional turmoil of it all!" she said. "I get the bathroom first. I am too tired to wait for anybody."

"You can't have the bathroom first, I'm already in here," said Marissa, closing the door on them.

Violet plugged in her hot rollers to preheat.

Brie opened the closet door and removed a long plastic bag in which hung a peach-colored formal gown, with satin sash, and ivory lace. From a shoe box she withdrew matching satin slippers. For the first time, Cathy saw, lying on Brie's side of the double bed, not the hotel's basket of hand lotion, and toilet water, and shoe polish cloth, but an old-fashioned bouquet of chrysanthemums, ferns, baby's breath, and lace.

Lace? thought Cathy.

Vi and Marissa shrieked when they saw the gown, abandoned bathroom and hot rollers, and held up the long dress, crying, "Put it on! Oh, it's beautiful! You'll look so pretty. Oh, Brie, I'm so jealous!"

"But what's it for?" said Cathy.

"The wedding," said Vi and Marissa, too absorbed by the gown to glance her way.

"What wedding?" said Cathy.

13

"I can't believe there's a party in my living room when I'm trying to find my daughter," said Claudia's mother. "Who are all those laughing people? Why don't they go home? I feel like going out there and shooting them all."

Jonathan hastily said that he would run out and play host, leaving Claudia's parents to deal with the missing child.

"Well, we've telephoned every single girl we can think of that Claudia is friends with, and either she didn't tell anybody anything, or they're being very loyal." Claudia's mother had been crying for over an hour. Her face was splotchy and swollen; her eye makeup, dark glops where she kept wiping at her eyes with tissues.

The police had said that, since Claudia had gotten on a train and left the state, all they could do was call the New Haven and the Boston police to look for her. They sounded bored, as though thirteen-year-old girls did this all the time.

The phone rang. "Yes, yes?" cried Claudia's mother, and then made a disgusted face. "It's Heather Anne, for you."

He had completely forgotten Heather Anne and the dear old friends. He told her everything quickly, before she got any madder at him.

"What do you want me to do?" said Heather Anne simply.

"Stay there. She might phone there."

In the room at the Hilton the girls jostled for mirror space.

"Claudia," said Vi in a strangled voice. "What—what are you putting on?"

Claudia stared at Vi. "My bridesmaid's dress." She looked down with pleasure at all the frills and ruffles, and twisted herself a little so the satin would whisper.

"Claudia, you can't wear that. You're a guest this time."

Claudia looked at the older girls. They were looking back with amusement and pity. Oh, they were trying not to, but they were laughing at her. I've worn the wrong thing! thought Claudia, completely demoralized, unable to look at any of them now.

Vi said kindly, "What else do you have, Claudia? A dressy dress? Or even a skirt and blouse?"

"Just my jeans and my sweatshirt." Why was it so demoralizing to be dressed wrong? It was only cloth, and yet the wrong cloth at the wrong time, and you'd rather be dead.

"Well, she can't go in that," said Marissa irritably, as if Claudia were offending her.

"Here," said Cathy. She wriggled out of her beautiful red wool sheath. Vi bundled the bridesmaid's dress back into Claudia's suitcase, and Cathy tugged her dress over Claudia's head. "But you're so tall," said Claudia, "and that dress is so long. It'll reach to the floor."

It nearly did. Vi tossed Cathy a belt, and Cathy secured it around Claudia's skinny waist. Then Cathy began hitching at the dress, pulling it up toward Claudia's chest. When the hem was the right length, she adjusted the top of the dress so it drooped down over the belt. Suddenly Claudia was wearing a sophisticated blouson dress that looked just right.

Claudia stared at herself in the mirror. If I had asked Heather Anne what to wear, she thought suddenly, I wouldn't have gotten it wrong like this. And they wouldn't have laughed.

"Dry your tears," said Cathy. "Hurry up. You need some makeup."

"Hey," protested Vi. "I do makeup around here."

They all began to laugh, remembering Vi at Camp Men. Cathy put on a white terry robe.

Claudia suddenly realized that Cathy was the only one not ready to go. "But, Cathy," she said. "What are you going to wear?"

Cathy shrugged. "I wasn't invited."

Heather Anne set down the telephone. She was suddenly horribly afraid. It was very dark out.

Very cold. Boston? What had made Claudia choose Boston?

She walked back into her living room and said unsteadily to her visitors, "I'm terribly sorry. My stepdaughter has disappeared. Probably run away. We—we don't know what we're going to do. They're having a conference at the other house."

How stilted it was to say "the other house."

I was mean, thought Heather Anne. Oh, I pretended to be nice. Fixing up her room. But I knew she hated coleslaw.

The dear old friends said they didn't mind, they would run along home, maybe get a hamburger along the way, not to worry about them.

Heather Anne had not been worrying about them. Pushing them out the door, she could hardly remember their names. She sat by her phone, wishing she could be with the others at the other house, in on the worrying and working. She wished Claudia would telephone *her* for help instead of *them*.

They were gone.

Cathy folded and refolded her T-shirt.

She closed the heavy drapes. The green room was as dark as a forest at night.

She could hardly tag along with them to the wedding. You couldn't decide that the hostess had done a lousy job with the invitation list and change it on your own. Certainly not a wedding and reception. Certainly not when Cathy had flirted with Charles over the summer, and had even made

138

a little headway, and Alicia reasonably enoug.. hated her forever.

How amazing that, downstairs, the kids had stuck up for her. Abandoned Brandon instead.

But Cathy thought that none of them were really her friends—not Marissa, nor Heath, nor Vi, nor any of them. They were the camp pledge. *A friend to people around me and to the earth.*

Generic friends, thought Cathy.

Like generic toothpaste, or generic spaghetti-o's.

If she turned on the television, it would be surrender. *I have no friends, but the boob tube will light up when I press the button. At least I can hold hands with the remote controls, and join in the laughter that came from a tape.*

I have to do something, thought Cathy.

She did not feel despair, and she did not feel contentment; she was in a holding position, and it was certainly better than the position she'd been in the last few months. The girls would be back after midnight, probably, and she would listen to them, and be on the fringe of their talk, and that would be better than nothing.

She resolved to go downstairs to one of the many restaurants in the hotel and eat supper by herself. Marissa and Vi and Brie would have a late supper at the wedding reception. Everybody in the restaurant would be a stranger. Doing things alone was easy when you didn't know anybody. The fear was that somebody you *knew* would see you alone, and say, Ah-hah! Nobody wants to be with Cathy; I could have told her that; I don't want to be with her, either.

She put on the clothing she had planned to wear in the morning. A long, tight jeans skirt with a kick pleat, a very large man's shirt in faded checks over a navy turtleneck, and a bright scarf and gold belt. I look like the back-to-school spread in *Seventeen*, she thought.

She decided on the Country Squire Café. Tables along one wall were meant for single diners, and there were half a dozen business people, men and women, sitting by themselves, reading newspapers or thrillers. She was almost hidden in her corner, what with the row of diners and the hanging plants.

Pink walked in with two men. He carried a briefcase. Each of his companions carried briefcases. Whatever else Pink might be, he was not an executive with a briefcase full of important papers.

Rage came in bright hot colors.

It was like lying on her back in the sand at the beach, the sun piercing her closed eyelids and setting off hot white flares in her head.

She hated Channing and Pink.

She hated them for their own ugliness, their own crimes, their own disregard of humanity. She hated them for dragging her into their sordid business, without even telling her. She hated them for using her and laughing at her and setting her up. She hated knowing that she had been just on dates, and the police and her parents and Brandon all thought she should have been gathering up evidence and drawing conclusions and stopping all drug traffic on her own between movies, maybe, or over strawberry sundaes.

Skunks! thought Cathy, staring at Pink.

She wanted to smash the little red candle-glass. Rip the menu to shreds and stab Pink with both her forks. She wanted to grab the pot of coffee a waiter was carrying and pour it in Pink's lap.

"Take your order, miss?" said her waiter cheerfully. He was a nice-looking young man, a little thin and tired, as if a long day promised only to get longer.

"An old boyfriend of mine just walked in," said Cathy. "He's the last person on earth I want to have see me. I don't suppose there's a way I can sneak out of here?"

The waiter grinned. "I don't think somebody with your looks can sneak anywhere," he said. "But I'll take you through the kitchen if you want."

She had made his day. He loved standing between her and the boyfriend. He loved shepherding her past the ovens and the deep fryer and the startled short-order cooks.

"Thanks," said Cathy.

"Hey, no problem. Always wanted to rescue a girl."

Strangers could be so nice. Impulsively Cathy gave him a kiss and ran on out into the hall. He probably wanted a tip more than a kiss, she thought. Oh, well. I was in a kissing mood.

She did not know if Pink had spotted her leaving the café or not. She had not wanted to turn her head and risk showing her face.

I wish there was something to do to stop rotten Pink, thought Cathy. I didn't know what was going on before. But now I know. What can I do? What can I manage—without getting smeared again myself?

. . . Marissa thought that when she got married, she would choose a room with windows. All the flickering candles in the world could not replace daylight. There was something dreadful about starting your married life in the half-light. Marissa wanted the blessing of sunshine for her wedding. She approved of the flowers, though: huge exuberant bouquets of chrysanthemums in every autumn hue—crimson, wine, and gold—shot through with color and joy and vibrance.

. . . Violet thought that when she married, she would have even fewer candles. Oh, the romance of dusk! So cozy, even in a big impersonal hotel room. The old-fashioned scent of the narrow white tapers wrapped the marriage with love. Vi disapproved of the flowers. Too gaudy. Vi would have only the most delicate of flowers at her wedding, and the palest of pastels.

. . . Claudia thought that if *she* had to get married someday (not likely, considering her views) she would skip all this wedding-ceremony junk. Oh, sure, it was nice to have a pretty gown, but Claudia would rather have dresses she could wear again, lots and lots of them, closets full of them, instead of one single white dress that had to stay in a plastic bag for the next fifty years.

"Dah dum da dummmm," sang Claudia.

Heath and Sin kicked Claudia.

Claudia snickered.

Marissa said, "I break bones, you know."

Trevor said to Vi, "Are you going to the reception?"

"Of course I am."

"Want to dance with me?"

"Of course I do."

"Are you a good dancer?"

"Of course I am." Vi gave him her pixie smile, full of mischief and delight. Trevor puffed out a long, slow lungful of air. The hair on his forehead danced.

Vi considered her next move thoughtfully and then put her hand in Trevor's.

Trevor considered her hand with equal thoughtfulness and then wrapped his free hand around hers.

Vi was just planning her next move—a slight, but definite, squeeze—when the wedding march began, and the guests got to their feet and turned to face the rear.

But instead of Alicia's cousins in peach satin, a huge, bearlike body suddenly galumphed down the *center* aisle—not one of the side aisles, like a late guest should—and shoved in among them, stage-whispering, "I can't believe I'm so late! My God, I used to lead compass hikes in the Maine woods, and I couldn't find my way to the Hilton. Can you believe it? Listen, how are you, Vi? Hey, Sin! Heath! Can't believe you showed up! Trevor! Guys! Great to see you all."

Vi felt fully responsible. Had she not prayed to the Lord God, to all writers of horoscopes, thrown coins in fountains, and wished on the first star that Jamie would show up?

Jamie leaned around Trevor, squeezed between Claudia and Vi, and planted a kiss on Vi's cheek. The kiss was noisy and smoochy and Jamie remained twisted over, grinning like an insane orthodontist's model.

"Ssssh," said Marissa fiercely.

"I have to say hi, don't I?" said Jamie.

"Trying to steal the show from a bride," remarked Claudia. "You should meet Heather Anne. She's your type. Pushy. Worthless."

"Shut up!" hissed Vi.

The music, luckily, was loud, and the aisle long, and one could hope the wedding party had not heard and had barely seen Jamie's arrival.

Brie walked slowly past, transformed by her pleasure and her gown from a stolid cheesy girl into a beautiful happy cousin. A very small friend of Alicia's and a very tall friend of Alicia's walked past, holding identical bouquets, both trying neither to smile nor cry.

There was a pause. The music strengthened. And Alicia appeared.

Alicia had no father and walked between her two brothers. Alicia was utterly beautiful, with her dark smooth hair and her ivory skin, her bright red cheeks, like a painted doll's, and her breathtakingly beautiful gown.

But mostly, Alicia was smug.

Vi bit her lips to keep from laughing. Alicia made no attempt to disguise the fact that in the great hunt of life, she was the lioness of the day. Alicia was preening herself every foot of the aisle.

As for Charles—who ran mountain expeditions

and taught waterskiing, who could cope with bed-wetting campers or the cook quitting on Parents' Day—Charles was scared. He did not look as if he would be able to utter a syllable, let alone vows.

"It's a good sign," Claudia informed them. "It means he's thought about what he's getting into. People like Jonathan and Heather Anne, they just spit out the vows like slogans for washing machine detergent. You know *they* aren't going to be there for richer or poorer."

"I don't want to be there for poorer, either," whispered Vi.

"Me, neither," said Trevor. "Let's get married for money."

They all sssshed each other, and tried not to laugh or talk once the organ music ceased.

But Heath thought, My mother married for money. And where is she now? All the money on the East Coast was ours for a while, and it wasn't worth it and never will be.

Heath thought about marriage.

The minister spoke of how married couples must deal together with the trials and tribulations of life.

Trials, thought Heath.

What does anybody here but me know of trials?

14

Vi remembered a day in camp when Jamie, out on the playing fields after the flag had been lowered and the last song sung, had picked her up and swung her twice in a circle before kissing her. All the campers had been in awe. That was love—being swung around.

Charles stumbled through his pledge to Alicia. Alicia sailed through hers. After the minister's pronouncement, the recessional began.

Vi thought: Being swung around isn't love. It's just somebody with muscles showing off.

The bridal party almost ran back up the aisle, the guests began snapping photographs, and the music got louder and louder. The room ceased to be a sacred place for vows and became a party, with everyone who couldn't reach their friends just shoving chairs out of their way to make paths.

Jamie made a fist and punched Heath lightly.

"Say, I keep reading about you guys," he said. "So how's it going, Heath? Huh? You hanging in there?"

"Sure am," said Heath, punching him right back, but not so lightly. "How about you, Jamie? Having a good year?"

"Oh, yeah, sure am, yup, didn't get on the football team, couldn't stick to those rules, you know? I mean, you'd think it was prison the way they expect you to get lots of sleep and never touch booze and keep your grades above a C."

Marissa stared first at Jamie and then at Vi. "Was Jamie always like this? I don't remember him being so stupid. He was always this terrific jock, out there mowing lawns and repairing roofs and canoes or being Daniel Boone for the little kids."

"We didn't talk that much," admitted Vi.

The boys all changed character, so they could greet Jamie exactly as he greeted them—loudly, with a lot of swearing and hitting.

"Did the summer Jamie turn into a different, less decent winter Jamie?" said Marissa. "Or did we make up the summer Jamie, and this was the guy all along?"

"Who cares?" said Vi. "I prefer to wonder why we didn't fall passionately in love with Trevor, who is a doll."

"Because Trevor was passionately in love with Cathy, remember?"

"It's coming back to me. Speaking of Cathy, Marissa. What about the reception? She'll be alone in that room for hours and hours and hours while we're down here dancing and eating."

"I know. I've been worrying about her since we left."

"It's a real burden being a nice person," remarked Vi. Acknowledging that she and Marissa were nice, however, took away a lot of Vi's worry about Cathy in the first place.

"Next year," said Marissa, "my resolution is to be mean and happy."

Heath had left his wedding present in his room. He slipped away to get it before going on downstairs to the Riverboat Lounge, where the reception was being held. At the elevators, a reporter caught his arm. "Why, it's Heath Hesper junior, isn't it?" said the reporter, smiling.

"Don't you guys have anything better to do than wait for me?" said Heath.

"Lots of stuff. I came here to interview a Japanese businessman about the economy and cover a meeting between a former terrorist and a current senator."

"Don't let me keep you."

"Well, as long as we've bumped into each other, I'd like to ask you a few questions about your father's plans."

Heath tried to circle the reporter, but the man just stepped alongside, so that they did a queer little dance right on past the elevators.

I'm reaching my limit, thought Heath. I'm going to deck one of these guys, even though I promise my mother every single morning not to antagonize the press.

Heath's fist, which had been aching to hit somebody since Jamie had barged into the wedding, doubled up again.

"I had a few minutes to spare," said the reporter, "and when I found out you were really here for this camp reunion, I kind of had a friend look into this camp of yours. Helps to have a rich father, doesn't it?"

"I was a counselor," said Heath through gritted teeth. "I didn't pay anybody. I got paid. And I earned it."

The reporter smiled. "So did Charles Crandall. Kept us reporters away from you, didn't he? Kept the TV news out, didn't he? Probably worth the Jeep and the minivan your father gave him to keep you out of view, huh, kid?"

Heath was moved beyond violence into shock. There *had* been a new Jeep and a new minivan at the camp. All the returning counselors had teased Charles for actually spending money on mechanical objects for a change. *Getting rich now, huh?* they had teased Charles.

That's my price, thought Heath. Or Charles's price.

A Jeep and a minivan.

Cathy thought camp was good. Well, it wasn't. It was just one more place where people were out for themselves.

Heath didn't know what to do. Going to the reception and speaking to Charles was out of the question. Going home was worse. Going alone to his room was impossible. Phoning Marissa, his favorite good-spirits technique, would not work.

Heath stood next to the reporter, like a victim waiting to be mugged.

Claudia was taking bets on how long this marriage would last. "Ten years?" she said. "Do I hear ten years? That's how long they last these days."

"Claudia, don't be sick," said Violet. "If we were at Camp Men right now, I would throw you off the cliff."

"Your mother agrees with me," Claudia pointed out.

"I'll throw her off, too."

"That's a lot sicker than betting on divorce," Claudia said.

"Claudia, just try to be a person," Vi commanded. "We are going to the reception, we are not taking bets on divorce at the wedding reception, do you hear me? Marissa breaks bones, remember? Do you want to go home in an ambulance?"

Trevor was laughing his head off. "I like your style, Vi. I don't know why I never did anything about it during the summer."

"You were in love with Cathy over the summer."

"I know." Trevor shook his head wonderingly, as if such thickness on his part was impossible to imagine in these clearer days.

Jamie bounded around having his own noisy, pushy reunion hours late. He was totally unselfconscious and completely unaware that everybody was hoping he would drop dead.

"*You* were in love with *Jamie* over the summer,"

Trevor said, in a voice that implied Vi's choice was far worse than his.

"I know. What can I say? Youth."

Claudia's parents attacked her room, hoping for a clue. She kept no diary, no date book. Mostly they found a lot of dirty laundry. Claudia's mother piled it in the hall, trying to get to the bottom.

"We sure won't find anything important on the floor," observed Claudia's father. "I don't think it's been visible since last year."

The phone extension in Claudia's room rang, and he seized it. It was Lynn's mother. "Lynn and I have gone over and over their conversations last night," she said. "You don't think—oh, I hate to suggest this—it sounds so crazy—but Claudia really loved camp, she was always telling us about it. You don't think she could really be heading for Maine, do you? Back to camp?"

Cathy marched across the lobby, trying to think of some way that she could get Pink. Oh, there had to be something she could do to the man! She paced past Reception and the ranks of elevators.

And there stood Heath—bones intact, upright position, but apparently in a coma. A reporter was asking him questions he did not even hear, let alone answer.

A reporter! thought Cathy. Reporters have their uses. They've used me and they've used Heath. Why should I not use one of them? She said, "Excuse me, Heath, you don't mind if I take your reporter for a minute, do you?"

Heath scarcely reacted.

"I have a *real* story for you," Cathy informed the reporter. "I know you like crime or you wouldn't be bothering Heath. Now I have a live, current, up-to-the-minute crime for you, as opposed to old, boring, last year's crime. And you have a camera. There's a drug deal going down right now in the Country Squire café. The man you want is the one two tables from the back on the left, with abnormally flushed cheeks . . ."

The reporter listened to Cathy's saga. "If you're setting me up," he said threateningly.

"Then you can come after me. Just don't reveal your source to Pink when you interrogate him."

The reporter was insulted. "I would never do that."

"You'd do anything," said Heath.

The reporter grinned. "Okay. I'll check it out."

He left, and Cathy pushed Heath into the first up-elevator. "Come on," she said. "We'll go to my room and call room service. Are you all right? You look ill."

"*Cherry Ames, Psychiatric Nurse,*" said Heath. "I never would have thought it of you, Cathy."

She giggled, breathless with her coup. She would sleep well tonight. She just hoped the reporter was good at his job. "Heath, I am improving. I can feel it. Character is growing away, inside me, taking root."

"Growing? Like in third grade, when you used to tell each other that if you swallowed a peach pit it would grow in your stomach?"

"Yes! I am turning into a good person, Heath."

"Siccing a reporter onto somebody is good?"

"It is if the person is bad."

Heath said, "This is too deep for me. I have to show up at this rotten reception for a minute, I guess, get rid of my gift, and then I'm going home."

"Rotten! What's rotten? Heath, they're all wonderful. Of course you want to go to the reception. Marissa adores you, and Charles and Alicia and—"

"Marissa told Sin every secret I told her. And Charles accepted a bribe in order to protect my privacy last summer."

Cathy was silenced.

They got out on the fifth floor and walked to Cathy's room. She opened the door with her key card, and Heath walked to the window, jerked the heavy drapes open, and stared out into the dark. "I guess I should thank you for the second rescue of the day, Cathy. It was good seeing you again, I hope you sort your life out—and I have to be going."

"Heath, please stay and share my french fries. Please?"

"Look, Cathy. I'm not hungry. I don't want to talk. I'm not going to ask you out, so don't flirt. Don't butter me up. Give me a rest, huh? I didn't ask you to barge in and I don't owe you anything."

Cathy glared at him. Did Marissa really want to take this husk of a person, stuff it back full of humanity, and try to prop it up? Yes, probably Marissa did. She loved a challenge. Cathy hoped that Sin would ask Marissa out first, though. Sin would be so much more fun.

"Listen," said Cathy. "I used to be ninety-nine percent bad and one percent good. Right now I'm striving for fifty-fifty."

"Aim high," said Heath sarcastically.

"But Marissa is ninety-nine percent good and one percent bad. You have to have a little bad in you or you're not human. Give her another chance. You need somebody you can count on, Heath."

"I can't count on anybody."

"Yes, you can. Let's go to the reception together. I bet Charles can explain the Jeep, and Marissa will be glad to see you."

"Sure, he can lie away the Jeep, and yes, Marissa will be glad to see me. Big deal. I just want to—to—"

"Hide," said Cathy.

Heath's fists tightened again. He had to remind himself that socking girls was not in his line.

"Let's not hide, Heath," she begged. "Let's play it's camp. I wasn't much of a camper. I wouldn't join in, or work hard, or help anybody. But camp enriched us all, Heath. Let's go to the reception. Come on."

"You weren't invited."

"So I'm crashing it. If you're right, Charles isn't a perfect person, either. Taking free Jeeps. What's a couple of hors d'oeuvres without permission compared to that?"

Claudia's parents started working through the stacks of paperback books, old school notebooks, treasures, old letters, and cassette tapes. Claudia had a Camp Menunkechogue address book some-where that would have phone numbers in it.

"Can you remember Vi's last name?" said Claudia's mother. "She was always telling me Vi was perfect. Maybe she went to Vi. Or called her. Or Vi would have a clue."

"I just can't believe she'd go to Maine. It's November. They probably have a foot of snow on the ground up there, and the camp would be completely boarded up. You can probably only get there with a snowmobile, anyhow."

"Oh, David, I don't know whether I want to hug Claudia a million times or kill her. How can she put us through this?" cried her mother.

He sighed. "I guess her argument would be that we've put her through a lot and we deserve it."

It was Heather Anne, attacking Claudia's other bedroom, who found the address book. She called Violet's house, and talked to her mother, and then phoned the other house. "There's a camp reunion this weekend," she said to Claudia's father, who answered the phone. "Violet's there now. It's at that new Hilton up the shoreline. Claudia probably told Lynn about Boston to make her jealous. I imagine she's eating hot dogs right now, telling those horror stories Vi taught her, and showing off her sweatshirt."

Claudia's mother was so relieved she could hardly stand. "I knew it," she said to her ex-husband. "I'm going to kill Claudia. No. You go get her and kill her for me."

15

Alicia was so excited and full of energy she could not bear to sit down, certainly not to eat roast beef, which is a heavy meal, and requires concentration and sharp knives. Alicia commanded the band to play—anything, as long as it was loud—and forced Charles to dance.

Vi thought the marriage was not off to a good start when one partner had to be forced to dance. But Claudia said it was off to an excellent start, because that same partner was willing to sacrifice, and look foolish in front of hundreds of people, being a totally inept dancer.

"He looks nice in that," said Vi dreamily, for even Charles was handsome when dressed for his own wedding.

Trevor said, "Come on, stop staring, let's dance."

Vi beamed at him. "There are probably only two

boys in New York State who actually love dancing," she said, "and I'm with one of them! What luck!"

"Luck?" said Trevor. "*Luck*, Violet?" He swung her out in front of people, and now the dress that Jasmine had picked was the right one, for the skirt was full and it danced by itself, spinning around her legs. "I am a true camper, you know," Trevor told her. "Always prepared. Got a Swiss Army knife with everything on it but a magnifying glass."

"Oh?" said Vi. She was aware of eyes on them. It was good to be the center of the action. She knew people were smiling. Trevor wasn't clumsy like Charles. Trevor was excellent. They were excellent together. It was going to be an excellent night.

"But I needed a magnifying glass, see, so I found an even truer camper. Charles. His Swiss Army knife, of course, has a magnifying glass."

"He's carrying a Swiss Army knife on his wedding day? The man is sick."

Trevor said, "So guess what I magnified?"

"What?" Vi took his hand and leaned back hard into the rhythm of the rock music, and their bodies rushed up close again, and parted with strength. "Oh, no," she said, realizing what had needed magnification. "You didn't?"

"Yes, I did."

Vi swung around and danced with her back to him for a few beats. "Oh, well," she said, swinging back, pretending the blush was from dancing. "Now you know. It was supposed to be a secret."

"What's the point of liking somebody if you keep

it a secret?" Trevor wanted to know. "I mean, you won't get very far that way."

When their bodies parted for some really violent footwork, a waiter carrying the first course passed between them. Soup. Trevor and Vi did not need any discussion to agree that dancing was better than soup any day.

As far as Claudia was concerned, the waiters could unserve the first course anytime. Probably had vegetables in it, soup usually did. If Claudia ever did get married, and was forced to invite people to a reception, she would serve food that people actually liked. Twinkies and Mallomars. Oreos and Reese's Peanut Butter Cups. Coke and Mountain Dew.

Alicia danced out of her new husband's arms and into the embrace of the best man. Charles danced with his mother, and Brie danced with an usher. Now Sin was dancing with Marissa, and now with Alicia. Marissa danced with Charles, and Vi worked her way through the line of handsome young ushers.

Claudia thought, I am the only one not dancing.

But, then, she was very nearly the only one there under sixteen. I personally am the young-camper-invite, she thought.

The music slowed, and the girls lowered their heads onto the boys' shoulders. The waiters cleared the untouched soup.

Claudia wondered what it felt like to dance. How did you know, the way Vi did, when to fling yourself about and when to rest on your partner's shoulder?

She wondered why the room was called the Riverboat Lounge. Except for three small circular windows with brass fittings, there was nothing remotely shiplike about it. The Hilton must have been very happy when Charles came to book his space. He was probably using more of the Hilton than IBM was.

Marissa's happy feet stumbled to a stop. For the second time that day, she stared at the couple appearing in the door. Heath and Cathy. Arm in arm.

Vi and her partner—an usher—stopped next to Marissa. "Just when you forgive a person," Vi said.

Marissa nodded grimly. "They sin again."

"Did I hear my name?" cried Sin. He was stuck with Brie and gladly let himself be diverted off the dance floor into a conversation with the girls.

Marissa pointed to the door.

"Oh, *that* kind of sin," said Sin.

"Well, we all half wanted to rescue Cathy," Vi reminded Marissa. Vi managed to leave her usher and attached herself to Trevor again. Trevor grinned. "Heath just acted on it."

Half wanted, thought Marissa.

"Oops!" cried Vi, "here comes Jamie, got to run, come on, Trevor, may I have this dance?" She and Trevor fled rather rhythmically. Sin put his hand on Marissa's waist.

Oh, why do I always yearn for the one I *don't* have? thought Marissa.

* * *

"There," muttered Heath, spotting the group just as Vi and Trevor danced away. "Now, listen, Cathy. Alicia's over there hugging some relatives, and Charles is at the bar with his bachelor friends. If we're quick, they won't even see us. We'll just slip right down there where everybody else is and blend in."

"We don't want to be quick," said Cathy. "We want to confront Charles and demand an explanation."

"Speak for yourself," said Heath. "I have had enough confrontations."

Cathy, to his horror, strode purposefully through the crowd of dancers, waiters, and guests toward the bar. Heath looked quickly around for rescue, but Marissa was dancing with Sin, and Vi was dancing with Trevor. There, in front of him, however, stood skinny little Claudia, staring wistfully at the beautiful teenagers and bridesmaids and ushers.

Claudia was the happiest person at the party. She was probably even happier than Alicia. Alicia *knew* she was going to be the center of attention, but Claudia had never expected such a thing. "I'm only thirteen, Heath," she protested.

"So what? I'm only seventeen."

Claudia found that neither of them could really dance, but that it didn't really matter. There were two of them, and they were moving to the music, and that was joy. "You're all right, Heath," she complimented.

"I don't even know why I'm here. When the music stops I have to leave."

"No! Please don't! When the music stops, dance with Marissa next."

"What is this," said Heath, "National Get-Heath-a-Girl Week?"

"No, it's camp reunion. Besides, you came late and you missed the announcement. You have to dance with everybody. Charles said so, and you're not allowed to leave until every woman here has been your partner."

This sounded so like Charles that Heath actually believed Claudia, and glanced around appalled at the number of women, their ages, and their waistlines.

Claudia giggled triumphantly. "You believed me."

"I thought you were trustworthy."

"Nobody's trustworthy," said Claudia. "Haven't you learned that yet?"

And Charles was between them, one hand high up on Heath's wide shoulder, one hand low down on Claudia's thin little shoulder. "*I* am trustworthy," said Charles. "Haven't you learned *that* yet?"

Claudia was embarrassed and giggled too loudly.

Heath swallowed, looking sick and angry, and looked away.

"Yes, I have a new Jeep," said Charles. "And a new minivan. Do you really believe your father bought them for me? Heath, I am truly insulted. You applied as a counselor. Your name meant nothing to me. In fact, I forgot your real name because Vi nicknamed you Dark the moment you

162

arrived. I bought that Jeep from a friend who had to move away. And I got a good deal on the minivan through the local dealership. It involved a trade: the dealer gets to hunt on my land in the winter. Your father had nothing to do with any of it. I've never even spoken to the man. A TV crew did come to the camp to interview you, and Alicia sent them off. And that's it."

Claudia's father and Heather Anne drove to the Hilton. "Now that it's over," he confided, "I'm more mad at myself than at Claudia. I think she may even have told us about this reunion and we didn't bother to listen."

"At least she's all right. When I was sitting there alone with the silent telephone, every time the house creaked, I thought of another terrible thing that could have happened to her."

They parked in the underground lot, came up in an elevator, and emerged in the sleek lobby. It was bustling with people. "What room is the Camp Menunkechogue reunion in?" Claudia's father asked at the desk.

"It was in the Mayflower Room, sir, but it ended hours ago. The room was cleared by six. And it's"—the desk clerk glanced at her watch—"ten-thirty now."

They were stunned. Claudia was *still* missing? "Could she be registered here for the night?" asked Heather Anne.

Claudia's father checked, but there was no Claudia Goodman registered. "Can you remember her?" asked Claudia's father desperately. "She was wearing a camp sweatshirt."

"Sir, I'm so sorry, there were dozens of girls and boys in camp sweatshirts."

David and Heather Anne stood in the hustle and noise of the lobby. People brushed past them, telephones rang, elevator doors opened.

Could Claudia have gone home with somebody? thought her father. Is she really running away after all? Is she so mad at us that—

He wet his lips and tried to think. Running a business was so much easier than bringing up a daughter. He and Heather Anne looked for the telephones, finding some down the hall that led to the Country Squire Café. "Eve?" he said frantically. "She may have been here, but the reunion ended over four and a half hours ago. What do you think we should do now?"

Vi's head was completely full of Trevor. She had danced with him almost every dance, and when they were forced to dance with other people, what with wedding etiquette, he waved at her. I'm in love, I'm in love, I'm in love! she thought. I knew it would happen one day. And it happened right here. At my reunion.

Reunion.

The word meant repeats. But for Vi, it was all new. Being in love with Trevor, and him being in love back, was new. Being friends with Cathy was new. Being the leader of the ghost rocks was new. She had never before attended a wedding for a marriage she was sure was going to last forever, and never before had she spent a night at a really magnificent hotel.

Marissa whirled by, dancing with Heath.

I did have a repeat, thought Vi. Marissa. We are going to be friends again, I know it. I will make sure of it. I'm not scared the way I was, scared of calling her, or of writing to her. Scared she didn't really want me to.

Her thoughts tumbled around, glowing, like hot dry clothes in a dryer, and she felt wonderful, and her head was resting on Trevor's shoulder, and she could dance forever like this, with no interruptions.

"Vi?" said Claudia.

Trevor stopped dancing. Vi wanted to keep going. I'm not your counselor now! thought Vi. Can't you see I'm very very busy? But she said, "Hi, Claudia."

"Listen, I really have to talk to you about something. It's a decision I'm making and I need your advice."

Vi sighed. "Okay. I'm listening."

Claudia looked meaningfully at Trevor. "It's private," she said.

I may kill you, thought Vi. This is not camp! This is life. Don't tell Trevor to leave.

Trevor said, "Okay, okay. I'll dance with the bride for a while." He grinned and threaded through the crowd. Vi watched him go. What a fine personality and a great mind and a terrific body he had. How could she not have noticed this over the summer? Where had her brain been? What had she been doing to miss Trevor?

"Vi?" said Claudia.

Vi remembered. She had been spending every waking minute with Claudia, and Janey, and Laury, and Dana.

"Let's go up to the hotel room," said Claudia. "We'll be very private there. And by the way, I can spend the night there, can't I? Sleeping on the floor? I won't be in the way, I promise."

Vi said, "Spend the night? Aren't your parents coming for you?"

"Well, that's what I have to talk to you about."

Claudia tried to pull Vi with her out of the reception, but Vi resisted. She kept looking for Trevor, but he had disappeared from view. Vi tilted back and forth, searching. Claudia asked her twice to come, and Vi barely heard.

Claudia gave up, and left alone.

That's three couples in one day who would rather not be with me, she thought. Mommy and Jonathan. Daddy and Heather Anne. Vi and Trevor. They all have better things to do.

Claudia wanted to sob for a couple of years, and break something big, like a house.

Vi would let her stay, but it would not be the wonderful slumber party Claudia had had in mind. She would be in the way. They would all want to talk about their boyfriends. Not about Claudia.

She had never felt so lonely.

It had been a strange day—wonderful parts when she was in control, and brave—and terrible parts when she was collapsing and unwanted. Claudia's feet slowed and she dragged herself toward the elevators.

166

"Okay, okay," said Vi, panting. "I'm here! You took off without me. Now start talking. What's going on?"

Claudia ignored her.

"Claudia, you can't get into the room without me. I'm the one with the key. Wait up."

Claudia waited. And there, across the lobby, going in the opposite direction, was Heather Anne. Headed for the Country Squire Café.

Those horrible rotten parents! They couldn't even come themselves. They had found out where she was and sent Heather Anne. Claudia could not imagine how they had located her. It made her feel like such a baby—having the perfect secret weekend away from home—and her parents just drove up. Only it was not her parents. They, of course, had important things to do. Parties to give. Heather Anne was good enough to drive over at night and fetch annoying old Claudia.

"Who's that?" asked Violet.

"Heather Anne. My stepmother. Oh, there's nothing I hate more than all of them getting along like camp buddies. Telephoning each other like sisters. Substituting for each other and carpooling. I hate them all."

Vi stared after the vanishing Heather Anne. "She looks just like me."

"I know. I hate her."

"Claudia!"

"I can't help it if she has hair like yours, Vi, and wears frilly clothes like you. She isn't you. Now if *you* had married Daddy, it would be different."

It certainly would be. Vi considered this novel

thought: herself as stepmother. She blinked, and returned to dreams of Trevor.

Claudia shoved Vi into the elevator and viciously punched the up button. "That does it, I'm really running away now."

"You are?"

"Yes. I just have to get my coat. I'll fix them. They'll never find me now. If they had stayed home the way they were supposed to, I'd have gone home myself. But no, they had to send Heather Anne." Claudia made it sound like a disease. She leaped out on the fifth floor, and dragged Vi into the girls' room. She ripped off Vi's belt and yanked off Cathy's dress. She tore open her suitcase and jerked out her jeans and sweatshirt and old sneakers.

Vi did not know what to make of all this violence. "What are you talking about?"

"And you don't care, either!" shouted Claudia, turning on her in a fury. "Well, I'm sick of it. If nobody cares, then I don't care!" This did not make sense, and Claudia knew it, and that only made things worse. She was crying now, too, and the tears made it hard to see the laces on her sneakers.

The desk clerk tapped on the glass wall of the phone booth that Claudia's father was using. "Sir? There was also a wedding. A Camp Menunkechogue wedding and reception. In the Riverboat Lounge. Perhaps your daughter is there."

A camp wedding.

How bizarre.

Claudia's father could not imagine what a camp

wedding might be. "Thank you!" he said fervently, and he and Heather Anne rushed to the Riverboat Lounge.

"Hi," said Trevor, ready to knock on the door to room 512 just as Claudia flung herself out. Claudia's thick sneaker sole crushed Trevor's toes, but she didn't say she was sorry. She raced down the hall toward the stairs. Trevor stared after her. "Vi, I thought you were just going to talk for a minute, but you left the party completely. Is something wrong? What's—"

Vi grabbed his hand and jerked him on down the hall after Claudia. "Hi, Trevor, I'm glad you came. Claudia! Claudia! Wait up! What are we talking about?"

Claudia flung open the fire door and pelted down the stairs. Vi dropped Trevor's hand, apparently feeling she could make better time without him, and tore after Claudia. Trevor got the fire door in his face, but recovered, skidded around it, and yelled down the stairwell, "What are you doing?"

"Running away!" shouted Claudia, her voice echoing up the long long shaft.

"From what?" he shouted back.

The girls were getting away from him. He had wasted time asking questions. Oh, well, thought Trevor, might as well follow through on this. It was hard to get up any real speed going down a set of stairs; all you could do was trot down each riser. Claudia, though, was going like a bat out of hell. Vi was yelling for Claudia to slow down and explain.

Claudia was yelling that she was through, through, through!

Trevor caught up to them a few steps before the lobby door. Claudia flung the door open. She and Vi burst out together. Trevor got the door in his face again, sidestepped, and leaped out, crashing into Vi, who had finally stopped running.

There in the lobby stood a crowd of assorted wedding guests, hotel guests, and employees. In front of them were Alicia, resplendent in her wedding gown, and Charles, red with rage and screaming.

"I knew it!" yelled Charles. "I knew you would do something, Vi. If it wasn't electric curlers and screaming at night, it was Mallomars and cheese Doritos! I knew you would start something at my wedding. You talked Claudia into running away from home. I'll never have you for a counselor again, Violet. I'll never give you a reference. I'm not even keeping your wedding present!"

16

"Okay, okay," said Charles, finally, after about a dozen different explanations. "So I jumped to conclusions. I'm sorry, Vi. A person does that around you."

Vi sniffed.

"Okay, okay," said Charles again. "I'll order pizza for everybody staying over at the hotel. Will you forgive me then? Pizza with everything for everybody?"

"As long as it doesn't have anchovies," agreed Vi.

Alicia's mother was storming around at the back of the crowd. "I told you nothing good would come of having a combination camp reunion and wedding. Runaway thirteen-year-olds, berserk fathers, Charles in a fit, that girl, Vi, throwing her shoes at him, that boy, Trevor, jumping between them to save Vi, and some reporter who's lurking around catching drug dealers photographing it all."

"Now, Mother," said Alicia, who rather liked the idea of being a front-page photograph in a newspaper, "I think it all went very well. Nobody will ever forget my wedding. And Claudia got the reunion she needed most—with her own father. And Vi and Trevor fell in love, at my very own wedding."

"Hmph," said Alicia's mother. "I think you should leave for your honeymoon before something else happens."

Alicia thought this was a very good idea.

Almost too fast for throwing confetti, it was over. Reunion and wedding had ended. Bride and groom had gone. First cousins and second cousins had retired for a postreception reunion of their own. The lobby was empty. Camp Menunkechogue boys and girls of any age had left.

Claudia sat wedged between her father and her stepmother in the front seat of her father's sports car. A wonderful thing had happened. She had not had to tell her father how rotten he was; he'd said it himself. He apologized a hundred times, insisted that he loved her, and even thought that it was all his own fault that she didn't have a ride home from the camp reunion. He figured she had told him and he'd just forgotten. Heather Anne had said she was sorry, too, and had promised never to serve coleslaw and to let Claudia redecorate her bedroom any way she liked. Then they had telephoned Claudia's mother from the hotel and her own mother wept. Her mother did not mention her ruined party or Jonathan. Just cried with relief that Claudia was safe.

This is how things should be, thought Claudia. I am the center of attention, and they are going to do things my way.

They drove through the centers of three towns. Christmas lights had been put on, and late at night the cities glittered and twinkled and sparkled.

"Daddy?"

"Yes, honey."

"I didn't tell you about the camp reunion," Claudia confessed. "I was going to run away for two days and see if you even noticed."

Her father winced. Claudia steadied the steering wheel. "Oh, Claudia, that makes it even worse. *See if we even noticed?*"

"But you did notice." Claudia smiled happily. "Everybody noticed." She remembered with pleasure the final scene, with people hugging and weeping and shouting accusations. Vi had even tried to throw things. Claudia loved it when people threw things.

"Claudia," said her father, "your mother and I promise to notice a lot more often. Okay?"

She patted his knee. She did not know where her own anger had gone, but it was nice to be without it. A year was a long long time to be furious. She felt rather light, and giddy, as if she had not eaten for days.

"How was the reunion?" asked Heather Anne.

"It was nice," said Claudia. "I think I'll go to camp again next summer after all."

* * *

Since the girls' room was the largest, they had the pizzas delivered there. Heath, Sin, Trevor, Cathy, Vi, and Marissa sat in a circle on the floor and ate hot pizza. Brie was still with her cousins. Mozzarella cheese strings ran from fingers to pizza boxes. Cathy treated them twice to more Coke from room service.

"I was thinking all day what different memories we each have of camp," said Vi. "There's nothing else that is silent and invisible like memory. You can see what schoolbooks people are carrying, and what instrument for band, and what coat they sling over their shoulders. But you never see someone else's memories. Even if you shared the same experience."

"Hey, she's a philosophy professor," kidded Sin.

But Trevor said, "I can think of something else that's silent and invisible."

"What?"

"Love," he said softly, then ruined the romantic thought by immediately stuffing a whole wedge of pizza into his mouth and smiling around it: a clown's face of tomato sauce and mushrooms.

"I have no use for love if it's silent," remarked Vi. "I like a love that comes right out and says, What are you doing Saturday night?"

The boys chewed pizza vigorously. First Cathy, and then Marissa, and, finally, Vi began laughing at them. The boys looked embarrassed, but determined to eat pizza rather than answer that remark. "They'll run out of pizza soon," said Cathy. "Then they'll have to answer." She was the odd one out.

174

Trevor would ask Vi, and both Heath and Sin would ask Marissa. But Cathy was neither sad nor hurt.

I am among friends, she thought. Friends because of camp. I don't know if they are lasting friends. But I have what I prayed for this morning. And I know I can be nice. I still want to be glamorous. I can't help it. It's fun to be a regular girl, wearing a jeans skirt and chomping down pizza. But I want to be a shining golden star. I still have to work that out. But I can, I know I can.

She said suddenly, "May I tell you about Channing and the drugs?"

They all squirmed uncomfortably.

She said, "It was glamorous. Not the drugs, but dating Channing. He had a lot of money, and we were always off somewhere being glamorous. I loved it. I never wondered how he got all that money, and I never wondered who all those people were giving those parties. I was wrong. I should have paid attention. I should have thought. But I didn't know about the drugs. I didn't even see them. I was just busy showing off."

They were not looking at her. Eating pizza suddenly had become quite a task, requiring a lot of thought and staring down at the wedges.

"So I'm trying to learn not to show off so much," she said. "Be a person and all. This is sort of my—well—my trial run. My first lap."

She waited.

And Marissa said, "You dressed Claudia. That was a good start."

175

"And rescued me," said Heath. "Twice. That was pretty fair."

Marissa set her pizza down. "Heath, I told your secrets on you and I'm sorry. Of course, it was just to Sin, but still—"

"Just!" squawked Sin. "I was a very important security leak, Marissa. I mattered!"

Heath said to Marissa, "It's okay. Sin—he's a good friend, too. I guess it wasn't so much gossip, as friend to friend. I—uh—have a hard time with friendship now and then." He flushed and reached for another slice of pizza. But they had eaten it all. He grabbed a napkin instead and crushed it.

Vi flung herself back on the carpet, her fluffy hair half an inch from Trevor's lap. "We're going to get weepy and worthless if we keep this up. It's because we're afraid we'll never meet again. It's now or never for confessions. So I am going to bring things back to the level of pizza and Coke. Everybody come to my house next Saturday. I'll rent a good movie. Do you think there's an Abbott-and-Costello-Go-to-Camp movie?"

"If there isn't," said Heath, "we could make one next summer."

"Heath! Would you actually go back and be a counselor again next summer?" cried Vi.

"Well, Marissa's going back."

He didn't add anything else. But the rest did their own adding. Marissa looked as smug and happy as Alicia had looked coming down that aisle. Cathy and Vi giggled. Trevor said he would bring the Coke. Marissa said she would bring a salad.

"Salad?" moaned Sin. "You mean we have to

176

have something nutritious? I am against nutrition."

Their talk went on and on, into the small hours of the morning. Brie never did show up. She must have found better company among all those distant relatives and twice-removed cousins.

Finally, awkwardly, the boys left.

There were no kisses, nothing but teasing, no good nights and no good-byes. The boys just backed out into the hall and then they were gone.

Cathy thought, there's another silent and invisible thing—friendship. And they gave it to me tonight.

She knew why there had been no good-byes. First, because Vi had given them all a second chance. Second, because they didn't know how to have a good-bye that was meaningful enough for all that had happened, both last summer and tonight—and yet not commit them to anything—like real dating. She turned to look at Vi and Marissa and knew that the foreverfriends needed to be alone.

She did another nice thing. She dropped her hopes for more girl talk and said she had to wash her hair and all, she'd be in the shower for ages, she hoped they didn't mind.

Vi slipped out of her clothes. Her figure was not a whole lot different from those of the twelve-year-old campers she had supervised. Very slowly, enjoying the slippery richness of the fabric, Vi slid Jasmine's ivory silk gown over her head and arms and shook herself lightly to make it fall the rest of the way. It was too long, and lay on the floor as if she lacked feet.

Marissa had forgotten about the realities of spending the night. She had omitted to pack nightgown or pajamas. She had even forgotten her toothbrush and toothpaste. That was what happened when you were sick with love for Sin and sick with guilt over Heath. You couldn't remember your toothpaste.

One good thing, she thought. I am over my crush on Sin. How sad, setting aside a crush that had never amounted to anything.

Violet handed over Jasmine's peignoir. "Wear this to sleep in."

Marissa put on the robe. She was taller than Jasmine, and had a lovely, curvy figure. She fastened the tiny satin-covered buttons, grateful that she slept on her back. All those bumps would be very unpleasant to lie on. Tiny ribbons circled the neckline like satin rivers, and broke into dozens of tiny bows at the bustline. Two panels of lace fell to the floor and met more rivers of ribbon.

Marissa ran her fingers through her hair so the long, thick dark curls fell against the gleaming robe. She stared at herself in the full-length mirror. This is how I will look on my wedding night, she thought.

Marissa had always seen herself as stern and sturdy, but now she was soft and romantic and infinitely desirable. She wondered to whom she would be married? Heath? Sin? Or a boy she would not even meet for years?

"How come you never wrote?" said Marissa.

"I'm not very good at letters."

"Yes, but it was *me*."

"Well, you didn't write to me, either. Or telephone."

We were each hurt, thought Marissa. We each expected the other one to go first. Why was that? "I guess I was afraid," she said slowly. "That you'd say you had better things to do. Or better friends."

"Well, I don't," said Vi, and they burst into tears and hugged one more time, and the tears were like cement—they were foreverfriends again. They told each other about school, and boys, and guessed about what might happen at Vi's next Saturday, and whether Sin's feelings were hurt, and if Claudia would be fine now, and how amazing that Cathy had turned out to have nice qualities after all.

There was a knock on the door.

They thought it was Brie, at last, and opened the door without looking through the peephole.

But it wasn't Brie. It was Sin, Trevor, and Heath.

Vi, a fragile mermaid in the long gown, and Marissa in her lace and ribbons stared at them.

"Wow," said Heath.

"Do we have to go back out?" said Trevor. "Or can we just stand and stare?"

"I could get my camera," offered Sin. "I figured you two wore Camp Men T-shirts to bed."

"We'd have come back sooner if we'd known this was going on," added Trevor.

"Nothing is going on," said Marissa. She felt naked. Ridiculous when nothing showed but her hands. All summer they had seen her in a bathing suit and she hadn't felt naked then. "Why did you come back?" she said.

The boys shuffled around and looked embarrassed. Why, they're sort of afraid of us! thought Marissa. We're glamorous. I bet they were going to take the plunge and ask us out—and now—

She was very glad there was to be another party. The boys might cut and run, but now she and Vi would have another chance. She made a mental note to dress without threats on Saturday—jeans and a shirt.

"Well, it's a good thing you showed up and you're still dressed," said Vi. "Go down to the little store near the newsstand in the back lobby and buy Marissa a toothbrush and toothpaste."

"You go," said Sin to Heath and Trevor. "I'll stay here and entertain everybody."

Heath just smiled. At Marissa. Her heart flopped over. "My treat," said Heath. "I never sent you flowers. Never bought you a great record or a new cassette. Let me get you toothpaste."

They all laughed.

And Marissa thought that she had loved camp, and she had loved this reunion—but next Saturday at Vi's.

That would be a time for loving.

Also by Caroline B. Cooney

SUMMER LOVE

Prequel to CAMP REUNION

'Wonderful job,' said Charles ... 'wonderful job, as always, Marissa.' He pointed to her, as if nobody had met her before, and the girls clapped. Marissa was trying to set an example of good camp behaviour for Vi ... because Vi would be too busy scanning the horizon for cute boys to notice them.

Boys thought Marissa.
There was only one boy in her dreams.
Marissa swallowed hard.
Camp, lovely camp, was no more than an unrequited crush on a boy across the lake ...

Her first night off. And what was she supposed to do with it? Write home? What was she supposed to say?

I wish I hadn't come.

I'M NOT YOUR OTHER HALF

'"We," said Annie, "will be chapter nine of every paperback romance we have ever read."'

When life-long friends Fraser and Annie both find boyfriends, they look set to make the perfect foursome. But Fraser begins to feel that gaining a boyfriend means losing her independence. Trying to fit Michael in with everything else she wants to do proves more difficult than she'd ever imagined.

Will she have to choose between love and liberty?

A thought-provoking love story.

DON'T BLAME THE MUSIC

'"I hate you," said Ashley. She spoke softly, intensely, like a hissing snake, and the venom sank into my mother and father. "I will always hate you. I would have been a success if it wasn't for you."'

Failed rock star, Ashley, arrives back home after three years of silence – and immediately starts tearing her family apart. Her younger sister, Susan, had been looking forward to an uncomplicated final year at school, but Ashley's outrageous behaviour soon invades every part of her life.

Then Ashley goes too far.

And the family realise they face a desperate and drastic solution . . .

Elissa Haden Guest

THE HANDSOME MAN

Fourteen-year-old Alexandra Barnes is falling
in love with a stranger, a handsome man in his
thirties. But what began as a romantic detective
game with her best friend Angela is more than
an infatuation; it's becoming an obsession . . .

Elissa Haden Guest

OVER THE MOON

'She was very beautiful, my sister, with light eyes and auburn hair. But there was a restlessness about Mattie, a sense of darkness. She was sixteen when she ran away with Dean Hartwell . . .'

After their parents' death, Mattie, Kate and Jay began a new life with their Aunt Georgia. Then Mattie left, shattering the family for the second time.

Now, four years later, Kate knows she has to find her sister. Travelling across country to Mattie's home is more difficult than Kate ever imagined, but it's a journey that will change all their lives.

Jean Ure

TOMORROW IS ALSO A DAY

Marianne, in her last year at school, is deeply in love with Abe, her blind musician boyfriend. Her mother decides it is high time she too had a life of her own. Marianne agrees enthusiastically until she discovers the object of her mother's affection . . .

Abe is now working with a glamorous soloist and concerts are arranged all over the country. But the tables have turned. He doesn't want to leave Marianne behind, especially now they are so close . . .

K. M. Peyton

PENNINGTON'S SEVENTEENTH SUMMER

Pennington can't wait to leave school. He's constantly kicking against the system, and if it weren't for his outstanding talents in music and sport, he'd be in even deeper trouble.

A series of confrontations – with the law, teachers, and his arch-enemy, Smeeton – means that Pennington has to fight his way to the end of the summer term . . .

'Pennington, the mean, moody and magnificent hero is that rare thing, an original heart throb'   *Daily Mail*

A Selected List of Fiction from Mammoth

While every effort is made to keep prices low, it is sometimes necessary to increase prices at short notice. Mammoth Books reserves the right to show new retail prices on covers which may differ from those previously advertised in the text or elsewhere.

The prices shown below were correct at the time of going to press.

☐	416 13972 8	**Why the Whales Came**	Michael Morpurgo	£2.50
☐	7497 0034 3	**My Friend Walter**	Michael Morpurgo	£2.50
☐	7497 0035 1	**The Animals of Farthing Wood**	Colin Dann	£2.99
☐	7497 0136 6	**I Am David**	Anne Holm	£2.50
☐	7497 0139 0	**Snow Spider**	Jenny Nimmo	£2.50
☐	7497 0140 4	**Emlyn's Moon**	Jenny Nimmo	£2.25
☐	7497 0344 X	**The Haunting**	Margaret Mahy	£2.25
☐	416 96850 3	**Catalogue of the Universe**	Margaret Mahy	£1.95
☐	7497 0051 3	**My Friend Flicka**	Mary O'Hara	£2.99
☐	7497 0079 3	**Thunderhead**	Mary O'Hara	£2.99
☐	7497 0219 2	**Green Grass of Wyoming**	Mary O'Hara	£2.99
☐	416 13772 9	**Rival Games**	Michael Hardcastle	£1.99
☐	416 13212 X	**Mascot**	Michael Hardcastle	£1.99
☐	7497 0126 9	**Half a Team**	Michael Hardcastle	£1.99
☐	416 08812 0	**The Whipping Boy**	Sid Fleischman	£1.99
☐	7497 0033 5	**The Lives of Christopher Chant**	Diana Wynne-Jones	£2.50
☐	7497 0164 1	**A Visit to Folly Castle**	Nina Beachcroft	£2.25

All these books are available at your bookshop or newsagent, or can be ordered direct from the publisher. Just tick the titles you want and fill in the form below.

Mandarin Paperbacks, Cash Sales Department, PO Box 11, Falmouth, Cornwall TR10 9EN.

Please send cheque or postal order, no currency, for purchase price quoted and allow the following for postage and packing:

UK	80p for the first book, 20p for each additional book ordered to a maximum charge of £2.00.
BFPO	80p for the first book, 20p for each additional book.
Overseas including Eire	£1.50 for the first book, £1.00 for the second and 30p for each additional book thereafter.

NAME (Block letters) ....

ADDRESS ....

....

....